Success

Assessment Papers

Maths

9 – 10 years · levels 3 – 5

Paul Broadbent

level showing
attainment target

paper number for
quick reference

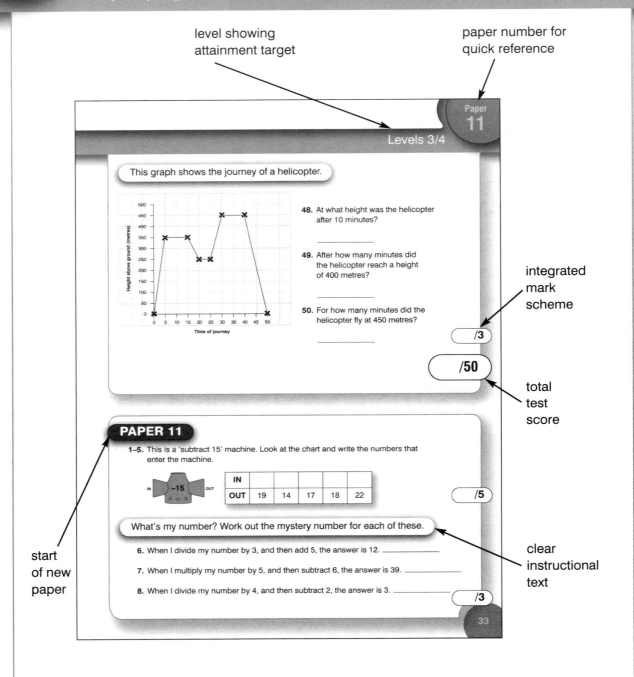

Paper
11

Levels 3/4

This graph shows the journey of a helicopter.

48. At what height was the helicopter after 10 minutes?

_____

49. After how many minutes did the helicopter reach a height of 400 metres?

_____

50. For how many minutes did the helicopter fly at 450 metres?

_____

/3

integrated
mark
scheme

/50

total
test
score

PAPER 11

1–5. This is a 'subtract 15' machine. Look at the chart and write the numbers that enter the machine.

IN					
OUT	19	14	17	18	22

IN −15 OUT

/5

What's my number? Work out the mystery number for each of these.

6. When I divide my number by 3, and then add 5, the answer is 12. _____

7. When I multiply my number by 5, and then subtract 6, the answer is 39. _____

8. When I divide my number by 4, and then subtract 2, the answer is 3. _____

/3

33

start
of new
paper

clear
instructional
text

Contents

PAPER 1

1. Write in figures the number one thousand and forty. _1040_

1 /1

Use these signs to make each of these correct: = < >

2. 3 x 8 $>$ 4 x 5   **3.** 2 x 9 $>$ 3 x 6

4. 5 x 7 $<$ 6 x 6   **5.** 4 x 8 $>$ 3 x 10

3 /4

6. Circle the two fractions with the same value.

$\frac{1}{4}$ $\frac{2}{10}$ $\left(\frac{1}{2}\right)$ $\frac{4}{10}$ $\frac{1}{3}$ $\left(\frac{5}{10}\right)$

1 /1

What is the difference between these pairs of numbers?

7.   500   380 _120_   **8.**   700   440 _260_

9.   400   190 _210_

3 /3

10. Circle three numbers that total 170.   (20)   50   (70)   (80)   30

1 /1

This clock shows the time at the end of a film.

11. At what time did the film finish? _7:40_

12. The film lasted 1 hour 20 minutes. At what time did the film start? _6:20_

2 /2

Each small square is 2cm x 2cm. What is the area and perimeter of the rectangle?

13. Perimeter = _20_ centimetres

14. Area = _40_ square centimetres

1 /2

Donna is making some biscuits. She puts flour on the scales and then adds some butter.

15. How much flour does she put on the scales?

_550 g_

16. How much butter does she add? _800g_

17. What is the total weight of the flour and butter? _1350g / 13.5kg_

+ **3/3**

Look at these 5 angles.

18. Which angle is a right angle? _d_

19. Which angle is an obtuse angle? _e_

20. Write the angles in order of size, starting with the smallest.

_c_ _b_ _a_ _d_ _e_

3/3

21. Draw lines on this shape so that it would make a cube if you folded it. Use a ruler to measure where they would go.

(/1

Draw each of these letters of the alphabet in full so they are symmetrical.

22.   **23.**   **24.**   **25.**

4/4

Jack has read 109 pages of his book and there are 32 pages left to read.

26. If he reads 8 pages each day, how many days will he take to finish his book? _4_

27. How many pages in total are there in Jack's book? _141_

2/2

All the digits 1 and 2 are missing. Complete these.

28.
```
    6 9
  - 3 6
  ─────
    3 5
```

29.
```
  1 6 8
  -   6
  ─────
  5 4
```

30.
```
    7 2
  - 5 7
  ─────
  1 5
```

2/3

31–34. Join the pairs that go together. One shape must be half of the other.

①

/4

Answer these problems.

My mother is 32 ...

35. My aunt is 7 years older than my mother. How old is my aunt? _39_

36. My grandfather is 30 years older than my mother. How old is my grandfather? _62_

37. My father is 5 years older than my aunt. How old is my father? _44_

38. My uncle is 4 years older than my father. How old is my uncle? _48_

9 /4

Write the next two numbers in each sequence.

39. 122   127   132   137   142   _147_   _152_

40. 185   187   189   191   193   _195_   _197_

41. 161   164   167   170   173   _176_   _179_

42. 144   148   152   156   160   _164_   _168_

4/4

Answer these.

43.
```
   149
 +  37
 ─────
   186
```

44.
```
   515
 +  29
 ─────
   544
```

45.
```
   268
 +  54
 ─────
   322
```

3/3

Measure the lengths of each rectangle.

Sorry for the Later

46. _____ cm

47. _____ cm

48. _____ cm

/3

How much water is there in each jug?

49.

2 litres

1 litre

_500_ ml

50.

2 litres

1 litre

1250
~~1200~~ ml

2 /2

40/50

-7: forgot to answer! -2 read question!
-1 wrong!

PAPER 2

34
36
25
‾‾‾‾
95

Use the numbers to answer these.

34   25   48   18   36

1. What is the largest <u>even</u> total made by adding two numbers? ___84___

2. What is the smallest <u>odd</u> total made by adding two numbers? ___73___

3. Which three numbers total 95? _34,36,25_

4. Which three numbers total 100? _48,18,34_

48
18
34
‾‾‾
100

/4

5–10. Look at the fraction of each circle shaded. Write these fractions in order, starting with the smallest.

 $\frac{1}{2}$ $\frac{1}{4}$ $\frac{2}{3}$ $\frac{1}{3}$ $\frac{3}{4}$ $\frac{1}{6}$

4   2   5   3   ←   1

smallest → $\frac{1}{6}$ $\frac{1}{4}$ $\frac{1}{3}$ $\frac{1}{2}$ $\frac{2}{3}$ $\frac{3}{4}$ largest →

/6

How many minutes are there between these times?

11. _30m_   **12.** `10·05am` `10·50am` _45m_

13. _1h30m_   **14.** `3·45am` `5·40am` _1h55m_

/4

15–22. Complete these multiplication grids.

x	7	9	8
5	35	45	40
6	42	54	48

x	3	5	7
10	30	50	70
4	12	20	28

/8

Complete these.

23. 2000g = $\boxed{2}$ kg

24. 5kg = $\boxed{5000}$ g

25. 4500g = $\boxed{4.5}$ kg

26. 6.5kg = $\boxed{6500}$ g

/4

Write the numbers shown on each abacus.

27.    1 5 4 7

28. 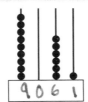   9 0 6 1

29. 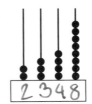   2 3 4 8

/3

A group of children were asked about their favourite activities.

This block graph shows the results.

30. Which activity was chosen the most?

_TV_

31. How many children chose swimming?

_13/14_ ?

32. Which activities were chosen by more than 20 children?

TV, Computer

33. Which activity did 17 children choose? _Football_

34. What was the total for using a computer and watching TV? _51_

25
+26
51

/5

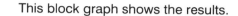
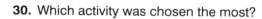

What are the halfway numbers on these number lines?

35. _355_
305 — 405

36. _310_
110 — 710 (+)

37. _516_
511 — 521

/3

Cross out the odd shape in each set. Name the set of shapes.

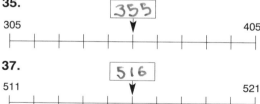

38. These shapes are all _Rectangles / cuboid_.

39. The odd one out is a _Pyramid_.

40. These shapes are all _cylinders_ ✓

41. The odd one out is a _cone_ ✓

42. These shapes are all _cubes_.

43. The odd one out is a _circle / sphere_.

/6

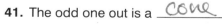

9

44. Write these temperatures in order from hottest to coldest.

27°C 40°C −12°C −4°C   _40°C 27°C −4°C −12°C_   /1

45–46. Circle the two fractions that are smaller than $\frac{1}{2}$.

$\frac{3}{10}$ $\frac{2}{3}$ $\frac{2}{5}$ $\frac{5}{6}$ $\frac{3}{4}$ $\frac{3}{5}$ /2

47. A square room has a perimeter of 36m. What is the length of each side of the room?

_____9_____   /1

A card shop sells cards at three prices:

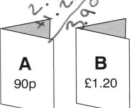

A	B	C
90p	£1.20	£1.50

48. What is the difference in price between card A and card C? ___60p___

49. Gemma buys three A-priced cards and a B-priced card. How much does she pay altogether? _£3.90_

50. The shop has a special offer of 50p off for any 5 cards bought. What would the total cost be for 5 C-priced cards? _7.00_   /3

46 /50

PAPER 3

1. Use each of these digits once to make a total that is a multiple of 5.

3 9 5 6   ☐☐ + ☐☐   /1

2. Circle all the amounts that you can make using only two of these coins at a time.

55p   32p   £1.15   50p   £1.02   /1

Write the fraction shown on each number track.

3. 0   1

4. 0   1

5. 0   1

6. 0   1

7. 0   1

8. Now write the fractions in order, starting with the smallest.

smallest → ☐/☐   ☐/☐   ☐/☐   ☐/☐   ☐/☐ → largest

/6

9–13. A group of children were sorted into these sets. Complete the table for the group.

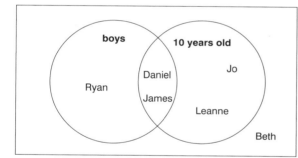

Boys		Girls	
Name	Age	Name	Age
Daniel	10	Jo	
	9		9
	10		10

/5

Write the missing numbers in each of these.

14. 69 + ☐ = 88   **15.** ☐ + 38 = 97   **16.** 92 − ☐ = 54   **17.** ☐ − 27 = 46

/4

Write the sign < or > to make these correct.

18. 704 ☐ 470   **19.** 492 ☐ 506   **20.** 285 ☐ 400   **21.** 610 ☐ 599

/4

Complete these.

22. 3 weeks = _____ days

23. 120 minutes = _____ hours

24. 3 hours = _____ minutes

25. 70 days = _____ weeks

26. 4 weeks = _____ days

27. 4 hours = _____ minutes

/6

Write the numbers at each arrow.

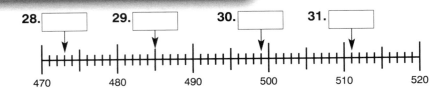

28. **29.** **30.** **31.**

470   480   490   500   510   520

/4

32. Circle the numbers that are multiples of 6.

18   23   56   54   48   61   38   16   33   42

/1

33. What is the value of the digit 7 in 7490? Tick the answer.

a) 7   **b)** 70   **c)** 700   **d)** 7000

/1

Answer these problems.

34. I'm thinking of a number.
If I add 8 to it the answer is 17. What is my number? _____

35. I'm thinking of a number.
If I subtract 3 from it the answer is 18. What is my number? _____

36. I'm thinking of a number.
If I add 40 to it the answer is 120. What is my number? _____

37. I'm thinking of a number.
If I take away 40 from it the answer is 20. What is my number? _____

/4

38. A pie is in the oven for 1 hour 20 minutes. If it is taken out of the oven at 6.00, at what time was it put in the oven? _____

/1

There are 6 birds' nests in a large tree. Some of the nests have 3 eggs in them. The other nests have 2 eggs in them. There are 16 eggs altogether. There are more nests with 3 eggs than 2 eggs.

39. How many nests have 3 eggs in them? _____

40. How many nests have 2 eggs in them? _____

/2

41. Circle the approximate area of this shape.

a) 8 squares   **b)** 7 squares

c) 9 squares   **d)** 6 squares

/1

The digits 1 to 8 are missing from these additions. Complete them with the digits in the correct place.

42.

```
   □ 7 6
+  □   2
_____
   7 0 □
```

43.

```
     7 □
+  □   9
_____
   1 2 1
```

44.

```
     8 □
+  □   4
_____
 □ 4 1
```

/3

45. Which of these is a symmetrical shape? Tick the correct answer.

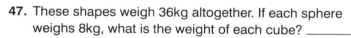

a)   b)   c)   d)

/1

46. Three pots each hold $1\frac{1}{2}$ litres of water. The water is poured into a 4 litre bucket. Some water is left in one of the pots. How much water is left in the pot? _____

/1

47. These shapes weigh 36kg altogether. If each sphere weighs 8kg, what is the weight of each cube? _____

/1

Complete these.

48. □ x 10 = 140   **49.** □ x 100 = 6000   **50.** □ x 100 = 9000

/3

/50

PAPER 4

1. Which number could be missing?

$374 > \boxed{} > 298$ **a)** 381   **b)** 294   **c)** 301   **d)** 260   (/1

2–7. Find a place for each of the digits: 0, 1, 2, 3, 4, 5.

$\boxed{} \times \boxed{} = 12$ $\boxed{} \times 5 = \boxed{} 0$ $\boxed{} \times 8 = 4 \boxed{}$ (/6

8. A football kit costs £47. What is the total cost for a team of 10 players? _____   (/1

Write these total scores.

This score is 36.

9.

10.

11.

_____   _____   _____   (/3

Look at these number patterns. Write the next number in each.

12.   420   425   430   435   440   _____

13.   840   845   850   855   860   _____

14.   1014   1016   1018   1020   1022   _____   (/3

15. If you start at 111 and count on in 5s, will the number 191 be in your counting pattern?

_____   (/1

Write the signs < or > to make these correct.

16. 33 x 2 $\boxed{}$ 23 x 3   **17.** 22 x 3 $\boxed{}$ 32 x 2   **18.** 32 x 3 $\boxed{}$ 33 x 3   (/3

Write these times.

19.

20.

21.

22.

_____   _____   _____   _____   /4

Write the number of faces for each of these shapes.

23.

square faces

_____

24.

circle faces

_____

curved faces

_____

25.

square faces

_____

rectangle faces

_____

26.

square faces

_____

triangle faces

_____

/4

27–30. Write the amount of water in each of these.

_____ ml   _____ ml   _____ ml   _____ ml   /4

31. A tennis racket costs £108. How much do two rackets cost? _____   /1

Draw beads on each abacus to show these numbers.

32.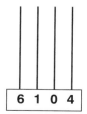

| 6 | 1 | 0 | 4 |

33.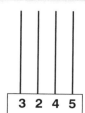

| 3 | 2 | 4 | 5 |

34.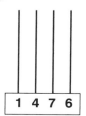

| 1 | 4 | 7 | 6 |

/3

35–40. What is the area of each shape?

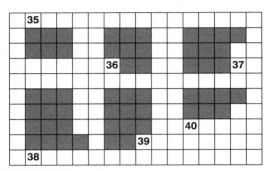

35. ☐ squares

36. ☐ squares

37. ☐ squares

38. ☐ squares

39. ☐ squares

40. ☐ squares

/6

Complete these.

41.	679	42.	762	43.	968
	− 137		− 201		− 454

/3

Circle the fraction in each set that is not equivalent.

44. $\dfrac{2}{10}$ $\dfrac{1}{5}$ $\dfrac{3}{9}$ $\dfrac{4}{20}$ **45.** $\dfrac{2}{12}$ $\dfrac{1}{2}$ $\dfrac{12}{24}$ $\dfrac{6}{12}$

46. $\dfrac{5}{15}$ $\dfrac{3}{30}$ $\dfrac{1}{3}$ $\dfrac{3}{9}$

/3

47–50. Complete this chart to show where David is facing after each turn.

Start position, facing:	Turn	End position, now facing:
home	$\frac{1}{4}$ turn clockwise	
bus station	$\frac{1}{2}$ turn clockwise	
shop	$\frac{1}{4}$ turn anti-clockwise	
school	$\frac{1}{4}$ turn clockwise	

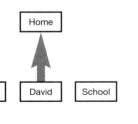

/4

/50

PAPER 5

1. Write the missing number. $50 + 65 + \boxed{} = 320$ /1

2. Screws are sold in bags of 20.
Robert wants to buy 280 screws. How many bags does he need to buy? _____ /1

3. Tick the two cards that total 4. $\frac{1}{2}$ $2\frac{1}{2}$ $3\frac{1}{4}$ $2\frac{3}{4}$ $1\frac{1}{2}$ $\frac{1}{4}$ /1

4–9. Write the letters for each shape in the correct position on the diagram.

	Symmetrical	Not symmetrical
Triangle		
Not a Triangle		

/6

Name each of the shapes above.

10. A → _____ **11.** B → _____ **12.** C → _____

13. D → _____ **14.** E → _____ **15.** F → _____

/6

16. Write the missing number to make this correct.

$\frac{1}{3}$ of 18 = $\frac{1}{2}$ of $\boxed{}$ /1

17–22. Join three dots on each grid. Make two different angles of each type.

Right angles   Obtuse angles   Acute angles

/6

Answer these.

23. $\boxed{} \div 5 = 10$ **24.** $\boxed{} \div 2 = 21$ **25.** $\boxed{} \div 6 = 6$ **26.** $\boxed{} \div 3 = 15$ /4

Use each of the numbers 29, 39, 5 and 4 to complete these.

27. □ × □ > 150

28. □ × □ < 150

/2

Answer these.

29. Ben and Amy walked to the shops. They left at 1:20 and they arrived at the shops at 1:55. How long did they take to walk to the shops? _____

30. Ali started eating his meal at 5:35 and finished at 6.20. How long did he take to eat his meal? _____

31. Becky went to the beach to collect shells. She started collecting at 6:55 and finished with a full basket at 7.35. How long did she collect shells for? _____

32. Sam started to paint a door on his house at 11.10 in the morning. He finally finished at 2.35. How long did it take him to paint the door? _____

/4

33–37. Look at this set of numbers. Circle the five numbers that are multiples of 9.

81   16   18   45   56   32   48   72   36   52

/5

This bar graph shows the number of children in a school born in each month from January to June.

38. How many children were born in June? _____

39. How many more children were born in May than in January? _____

40. In which month were 16 children born? _____

41. How many children in total were born in January and February? _____

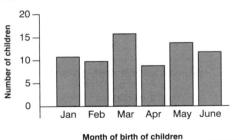

Month of birth of children

/4

42–47. Draw a line to match each fraction with the correct place on this number line.

$\frac{3}{5}$ $\frac{1}{10}$ $\frac{7}{10}$ $\frac{2}{5}$ $\frac{9}{10}$ $\frac{1}{2}$

0   1

/6

Calculate the perimeter of each of these. The lengths given are not the actual lengths.

 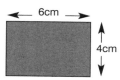 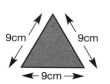

48. _____   49. _____   50. _____   /3

/50

PAPER 6

Write the number that is one more than each of these.

1. 9009 _____ **2.** 9909 _____ **3.** 9099 _____ **4.** 9990 _____   /4

Answer these.

5.   946
       + 677
       _____

       _____

6.   745
       − 359
       _____

       _____

7.   4706
       + 388
       _____

       _____

8.   3152
       − 678
       _____

       _____

/4

Look at these patterns. Write the next two numbers.

9–10.   5650   5750   5850   _____ _____

11–12.   1423   1433   1443   _____ _____

13–14.   4029   5029   6029   _____ _____   /6

15. If you start at 240 and count on in 50s, will
the number 590 be in your counting pattern? _____   /1

16. A clock runs slow and loses 10 minutes every hour. If it is put at the correct
time at 5.00pm, what time will the clock say in 4 hours time? _____   /1

Answer these.

| 17. | 19
x 4
——
—— | 18. | 26
x 3
——
—— | 19. | 35
x 6
——
—— | 20. | 57
x 5
——
—— |

/4

21–24. Answer these.

21. 3⟌84　　**22.** 4⟌52　　**23.** 6⟌90　　**24.** 2⟌76

/4

25–28. Tick the shapes that are symmetrical.

/4

29–36. Complete this chart. For each shape, draw each of its different faces.

Shape	Name	Faces

/8

What's my number? Work out the mystery number for each of these.

37. When I divide my number by 4, and then add 2, the answer is 4. _____

38. When I multiply my number by 3, and then subtract 5, the answer is 16. _____

39. When I divide my number by 5, and then subtract 1, the answer is 2. _____

/3

Complete these.

40. 3km = ☐ m   **41.** 800cm = ☐ m   **42.** 7000m = ☐ km

43. 8m = ☐ cm   **44.** 750cm = ☐ m   **45.** $3\frac{1}{2}$ km = ☐ m   /6

46. Jamie is posting three parcels. Each is a different weight.

The first and second parcels weigh 6kg altogether. The third parcel weighs 1kg more than the first parcel. The first and third parcels weigh 9kg altogether. What is the weight of each parcel?

Parcel 1 → _____   Parcel 2 → _____   Parcel 3 → _____   /1

Draw rectangles with these areas.

47. 18 squares

48. 20 squares   /2

Tick the shape that shows an equivalent fraction to the following:

49. $\frac{1}{2}$ **50.** $\frac{1}{4}$    /2

/50

PAPER 7

1–5. Write the numbers at each arrow.

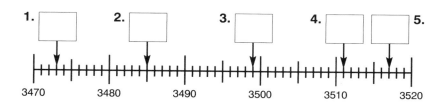

1. ☐   **2.** ☐   **3.** ☐   **4.** ☐ ☐   **5.**

/5

3470   3480   3490   3500   3510   3520

Circle the fraction in each set that is *not* equivalent to the others.

6. $\dfrac{4}{20}$ $\dfrac{4}{16}$ $\dfrac{6}{24}$ $\dfrac{1}{4}$

7. $\dfrac{3}{16}$ $\dfrac{1}{8}$ $\dfrac{3}{24}$ $\dfrac{4}{32}$

8. $\dfrac{3}{4}$ $\dfrac{3}{12}$ $\dfrac{4}{16}$ $\dfrac{1}{4}$

/3

Write the missing numbers in these sequences.

9–10. 800 ☐ 900 950 1000 ☐

11–12. 120 ☐ 320 420 ☐ 620

13–14. 1030 1035 ☐ ☐ 1050 1055

15–16. 1410 1510 ☐ 1710 1810 ☐

/8

Write the time that is:

17. 40 minutes later than 4.25pm. _____

18. 25 minutes later than 8.50am. _____

19. 20 minutes earlier than 11.50am. _____

20. 45 minutes earlier than 5.20pm. _____

/4

This pictogram shows the number of books sold from a shop each day for a week.

Monday	📖📖📖📖📖
Tuesday	📖📖📖📖📖📖📖📖📖
Wednesday	📖📖📖📖📖📖📖📖📖📖📖📖📖
Thursday	📖📖📖📖📖📖📖📖📖
Friday	📖📖📖📖📖📖📖
Saturday	📖📖📖📖📖📖📖📖
Sunday	📖📖📖📖📖

Key:  represents 5 books

21. How many books were sold in total on Tuesday? _____

22. On which day were 45 books sold? _____

23. How many more books were sold on Wednesday than on Monday? _____

24. How many books were sold altogether on Saturday and Sunday? _____

/4

25. There are 36 balls in a box. $\frac{1}{3}$ of them are red, $\frac{1}{6}$ of them are blue and the rest of them are green. How many of the balls are green? _____   /1

Complete these.

26. $7 \times \boxed{} = 28$ **27.** $\boxed{} \times 6 = 18$ **28.** $6 \times \boxed{} = 36$ **29.** $\boxed{} \times 9 = 45$ /4

30–34. This dial has four positions A, B, C and D. Complete this chart to show the start and finish positions for each turn.

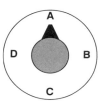

Start position	Turn	End position
A	$\frac{1}{4}$ turn anticlockwise	
C	$\frac{3}{4}$ turn clockwise	
B	$\frac{1}{4}$ turn anticlockwise	
A	$\frac{1}{4}$ turn clockwise	
D	$\frac{1}{2}$ turn anticlockwise	

/5

Look at the sets of triangles. Name each set.

A    B    C

35. _____   **36.** _____   **37.** _____

/3

Tick to show whether each angle is acute, obtuse or right-angled.

Angle	38.	39.	40.	41.	42.	43.
Acute						
Obtuse						
Right-angled						

38.   **39.**   **40.**

41.   **42.**   **43.**

/6

23

Complete these, writing in the correct signs = < or >.

44. 3 x 8 ☐ 25   **45.** 48 ÷ 3 ☐ 16   **46.** 9 x 6 ☐ 52   **47.** 65 ÷ 5 ☐ 15   /4

Complete these.

48. $6\frac{1}{2}$ kg = ☐ g   **49.** 4250g = ☐ kg   **50.** 750g = ☐ kg   /3

/50

PAPER 8

Read these and write each as a number.

1. eight thousand nine hundred and twenty-five   _____

2. six thousand four hundred and seventy-nine   _____

3. four thousand eight hundred and thirty-four   _____

4. nine thousand five hundred and sixty-one   _____   /4

5–12. Complete the chart, rounding to the nearest 10 and 100.

	Round to the nearest 10	Round to the nearest 100
4148 →		
3691 →		
6037 →		
5689 →		

/8

Answer these.

13. There are 289 children in Robert's school and 393 children in Ali's school. How many children are there in total in the two schools? _____

14. A lorry travels 156km to collect vegetables from a farm and 147km back to the market in the town. How far does the lorry travel in total? _____

15. Rachid scored 519 points on a video game. Tom scored 638 more points than Rachid. How many points did Tom score? _____

16. A table cost £670, and a set of chairs cost £397. How much is this in total? _____

17–18. Complete these, writing in the digits 1, 2, 3, 4, 5 and 6.

$$\begin{array}{r} \square\,8\,3 \\ -\ \ 5\,\square\,8 \\ \hline 1\,6\,\square \end{array} \qquad \begin{array}{r} 8\,\square\,9 \\ -\ \ 4\,3\,\square \\ \hline \square\,9\,5 \end{array}$$

These are the lengths of some of the longest rivers in the world. Answer these questions.

River Name	Continent	Length in kilometres
Nile	Africa	6690km
Amazon	S. America	6387km
Mississippi	N. America	6270km
Chang Jiang	Asia	6211km
Congo	Africa	4371km
Niger	Africa	4167km

19. What is the difference in length between the two longest rivers in the world, the Nile and the Amazon? _____

20. How much longer is the Nile than the Niger? _____

21. Which two rivers have a difference of 117km? _____

22. How much shorter is the Niger than the Congo? _____

23. Which river is 2319km shorter than the Nile? _____

24. Which two rivers have the smallest difference between them? _____

25–29. Write the name of each of these shapes from its net.

25. _____ **26.** _____ **27.** _____ **28.** _____ **29.** _____

/5

30–34. Draw each shape on the diagram.

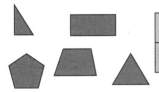

	Symmetrical	Not symmetrical
Triangle		
Not a Triangle		

/5

John used some bricks to build a barbecue. The bricks were a mixture of two weights: 3kg and 4kg. He used one more 3kg brick than the number of 4kg bricks and altogether the bricks weighed 45kg.

35. How many of them were 3kg bricks?_____

36. How many of them were 4kg bricks?_____

/2

37. Perimeter of rectangle = _____ cm

38. Perimeter of triangle = _____ cm

39. The shape with the greater perimeter is the _____ .

/3

Calculate the area of these rectangles.

40.

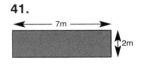

41.

42.

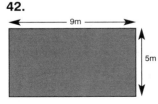

43.

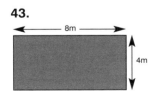

Area = _____ m²   Area = _____ m²   Area = _____ m²   Area = _____ m²

/4

44. A film starts at 7.55pm. It lasts for 2 hours and 10 minutes.

What time will the film finish?_____   /1

Choose two of these digit cards each time to make the following 2 digit numbers.

⑤ ⑧ ⑥ ①

45. An odd number ➔_____   **46.** A multiple of 8 ➔_____

47. A square number ➔_____   /3

48. What is 7/10 as a percentage? Tick the correct answer.

    a) 7%   **b)** 30%   **c)** 70%   **d)** 170%   /1

49. Put a circle around the numbers that are factors of 18.   7 9 3 4 6 2 12   /1

50. What time will this clock show in 30 minutes? _____   **13.55**   /1

/50

PAPER 9

Circle the smallest number and underline the largest number in each group.

1.   8102   8201   8211   8101   **2.**   5956   5965   5955   5966

3.   4080   4089   4806   4803   /3

Complete these.

4. 7 x ☐ = 21   **5.** ☐ x 4 = 32   **6.** 5 x ☐ = 45

7. ☐ x 3 = 27   **8.** 6 x ☐ = 36   **9.** ☐ x 9 = 72   /6

Look at this bus timetable.

	Bus A	Bus B	Bus C	Bus D
School	8.15am	9.35am	11.05am	1.55pm
Hospital	8.35am	9.50am	11.30am	2.15pm
Market	8.45am	10.00am	11.40am	2.35pm
Town Centre	9.10am	10.30am	12.05pm	2.45pm

10. What time does Bus B leave the school? _____

11. Which bus arrives at the market at this time? _____

12. Which bus do you need to catch to arrive at the hospital at this time? _____

13. How long is the journey from the hospital to the town centre on Bus B? _____

14. Which is the quickest bus from the school to the town centre? _____   /5

Draw the lines of symmetry on each shape.

15.   **16.**    **17.**   **18.**    **19.**   /5

20–31. Count the edges, faces and vertices on each shape and complete the chart.

Shape	Name	Faces	Edges	Vertices

/12

Complete these.

32. $2 \times \boxed{} + 5 = 19$ **33.** $3 \times \boxed{} - 4 = 23$ **34.** $5 \times \boxed{} - 3 = 17$ **35.** $4 \times \boxed{} + 5 = 29$ /4

Answer these.

36. There is a box of 18 bottles waiting to be filled with drinking water. If each bottle contains 3 litres, how much water is needed to fill all the bottles? _____

37. Two pipes are 1m 85cm and 2m 62 cm in length. What is the difference in their lengths? _____

38. James bought 5 sacks of flour from a mill. Each sack weighed 18 kg. What was the total weight of the flour? _____

39. A crate of bananas weighed 53kg when it was full. When the bananas were taken out, the crate weighed 8kg. What was the total weight of the bananas? _____

40. A length of rope 2m 52cm is cut into 4 equal lengths. How long is each piece? _____

41. The rule for this number sequence is double and then add 3. What is the next number in the sequence?   5   13   29   61   _____ /6

42. What is 50% of £30? _____ /1

43. A spoonful is 5ml. How many spoonfuls can you get from this bottle? _____ /1

44. Put a cross on the shape that is not a net of a square based pyramid.

/1

Calculate the perimeter of each of these.

45.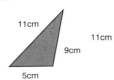

11cm
11cm
9cm
5cm

46.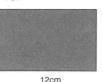

12cm

47.

8cm
8cm

48.

14cm   14cm
9cm

/4

_____ cm   _____ cm   _____ cm   _____ cm

49. A 1 litre bottle is $\frac{1}{4}$ full of juice and a 600ml bottle is $\frac{1}{2}$ full of juice. Circle the bottle that contains the most juice.

/1

50. In a shop a t-shirt costs £14 and a jumper costs £18.50. There is a half-price sale, so what is the new total price for the two items? _____

/1

/50

PAPER 10

1–6. Write the fraction each arrow is pointing to. Simplify the fractions if needed.

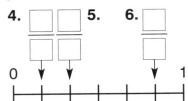

1. ☐/☐ **2.** ☐/☐ **3.** ☐/☐ **4.** ☐☐/☐☐ **5.** ☐/☐ **6.** ☐/☐

/6

Complete these.

7. 8000g = ☐ kg

8. 9kg = ☐ g

9. 3500g = ☐ kg

10. $2\frac{1}{2}$ kg = ☐ g

11. $\frac{1}{4}$ kg = ☐ g

12. 1750g = ☐ kg

/6

13. What is the smallest number that leaves: a remainder of 1 when divided by 2; a remainder of 2 when divided by 3; a remainder of 3 when divided by 4; a remainder of 5 when divided by 6? _____

/1

Answer these.

14. 37
x 4
_____

_____

15. 56
x 3
_____

_____

16. 89
x 5
_____

_____

17. 74
x 6
_____

_____

/4

Calculate the area and perimeter of each of these rectangles.

3cm

9cm

7cm

8cm

6cm

11cm

18. Area = _____

20. Area = _____

22. Area = _____

19. Perimeter = _____

21. Perimeter = _____

23. Perimeter = _____   /6

Answer these.

24. A market stall opens at 8.45am and closes at 1.25pm.
How long was the stall open for? _____

25. Mr Jones drove a lorry from 6.55am until 8.10am before taking a rest.
How long had he been driving for? _____

26. Robert ran a half-marathon and finished in 1 hour 35 minutes.
If the race started at 10.15am, what time did he finish? _____

27. A flight from Manchester to Rome takes 2 hours 45 minutes. The 1.20pm departure
is delayed by 40 minutes. What time will it now land in Rome? _____   /4

Write the missing numbers in these sequences.

28.   1700   1800   ☐   ☐   2100   ☐   2300

29.   508   ☐   504   502   ☐   ☐   496

30.   3245   ☐   ☐   ☐   3265   3270   3275

31.   2050   ☐   ☐   2200   2250   ☐   2350   /4

Answer these.

32.   9254
        + 631
        _____

        _____

33.   8326
        + 649
        _____

        _____

34.   3703
        + 195
        _____

        _____

35.   7170
        + 343
        _____

        _____   /4

The digits 1, 2, 3 and 4 are missing from these. Complete these.

36.

$$\begin{array}{r} 7\ 9\ \square \\ -\ \square\ 8\ 1 \\ \hline 5\ 1\ 3 \end{array}$$

37.

$$\begin{array}{r} 8\ 4\ 8 \\ -\ 6\ \square\ 5 \\ \hline 2\ 3\ \square \end{array}$$

/2

38–40. Draw two more sides to complete each triangle.

isosceles triangle   equilateral triangle   right-angled triangle

/3

Tick to show whether each angle is acute, obtuse or right-angled.

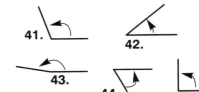
41. **42.**

43. **44.** **45.**

Angle	41.	42.	43.	44.	45.
Acute					
Obtuse					
Right-angled					

/5

46. Peter jumped 2.08cm on his second try at the long jump. This was 46cm longer than his first jump. How far did he jump on his first try? Circle the correct answer.

a) 1m 58cm   **b)** 1m 62cm   **c)** 1 m 54cm   **d)** 2m 54cm

/1

47. Write the missing colours on this spinner so that you are more likely to spin red than blue.

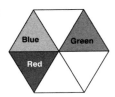

/1

This graph shows the journey of a helicopter.

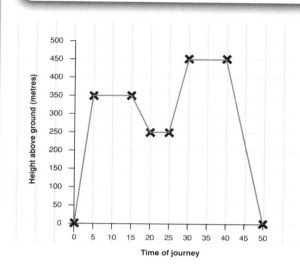

48. At what height was the helicopter after 10 minutes?

_____

49. After how many minutes did the helicopter reach a height of 400 metres?

_____

50. For how many minutes did the helicopter fly at 450 metres?

_____

/3

/50

PAPER 11

1–5. This is a 'subtract 15' machine. Look at the chart and write the numbers that enter the machine.

IN					
OUT	19	14	17	18	22

/5

What's my number? Work out the mystery number for each of these.

6. When I divide my number by 3, and then add 5, the answer is 12. _____

7. When I multiply my number by 5, and then subtract 6, the answer is 39. _____

8. When I divide my number by 4, and then subtract 2, the answer is 3. _____

/3

33

9. If you started at 50 on a number line and jumped back in 4s, would you land on zero?   /1

_____

10–13. Draw the total weight on each weighing scale.

/4

Write the equivalent fractions shown on each number track.

14. 0 _____ 1 $\dfrac{2}{\Box} = \dfrac{\Box}{2}$

15. 0 _____ 1 $\dfrac{2}{\Box} = \dfrac{\Box}{3}$

16. 0 _____ 1 $\dfrac{6}{\Box} = \dfrac{\Box}{4}$

17. 0 _____ 1 $\dfrac{4}{\Box} = \dfrac{\Box}{3}$

/4

18. Write the correct sign, <, > or = for this. $\frac{2}{5}$ of £50 ☐ $\frac{2}{3}$ of £30   /1

19. Circle the time that is the same as 14.40.   4.40pm   4.40am   2.40am   2.40pm   /1

20. Put a circle around the approximate mass of an orange.

    2.5g   5g   25g   250g   1500g   2500g   /1

21. This square has a diagonal drawn on it.
What is the size of angle x? _____°   /1

22. What is the missing number?   23 x ☐ = 4600   /1

Answer each of these.

23. $\frac{3}{10}$ of 30kg = ☐   24. $\frac{2}{5}$ of £20 = ☐   25. $\frac{2}{3}$ of £21 = ☐

26. $\frac{5}{6}$ of 18m = ☐   27 $\frac{3}{4}$ of 24l = ☐   28. $\frac{5}{8}$ of 16kg = ☐   /6

Each week Rosie has a spelling test, with 20 words to learn for each test. This graph shows her results for 6 weeks.

29. In which week did she get 19 out of 20 in her test?

_____

30. How many words did she spell correctly on week 6? _____

31. In which week did she score 14 out of 20?

_____

32. In which week did she make 6 mistakes with her spellings? _____

33. How many more words did she spell correctly in week 3 than in week 4? _____

34. In which week did she get ¾ of her spellings correct? _____

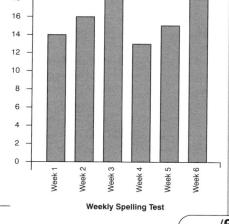

Weekly Spelling Test

/6

35–36. Measure the shortest and longest sides of this shape. Measure them accurately in millimetres.

Shortest side is _____mm.

Longest side is _____mm.

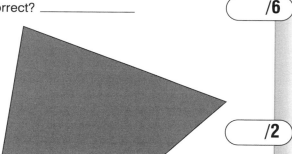

/2

Complete these equivalent fraction chains. Look for the patterns.

37. $\dfrac{1}{2} = \dfrac{2}{\square} = \dfrac{\square}{6} = \dfrac{4}{\square} = \dfrac{\square}{10}$

38. $\dfrac{2}{3} = \dfrac{\square}{6} = \dfrac{6}{\square} = \dfrac{\square}{12} = \dfrac{10}{\square}$

39. $\dfrac{3}{4} = \dfrac{6}{\square} = \dfrac{\square}{12} = \dfrac{12}{\square} = \dfrac{\square}{20}$

/3

Choose any of the numbers in the box to complete each of these. | 4 7 9 11 |

40. 6 x ☐ < 40   **41.** 26 − ☐ < 19   **42.** 42 ÷ ☐ = 6

43. ☐ + 8 > 15   **44.** ☐ x 9 > 80   **45.** ☐ − 3 > 5

/6

46–50. Join each of these shapes to their matching name.

Cuboid   Cylinder   Sphere   Pyramid   Cone

/5

/50

PAPER 12

Write the numbers at each arrow.

1. ☐   **2.** ☐   **3.** ☐ ☐   **4.**   **5.** ☐

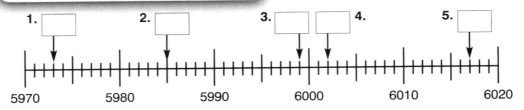

5970   5980   5990   6000   6010   6020

/5

Answer these.

6. What is 377 subtract 243? _____

7. What is 423 more than 952? _____

8. What is 896 take away 722? _____

9. What is the difference between 784 and 811? _____

10. What is 958 added to 175? _____

11. What is the total of 814 and 663? _____

/6

Answer booklet Maths 9–10

PAPER 1
1. 1040
2. >
3. =
4. <
5. >
6. $\frac{1}{2}, \frac{5}{10}$
7. 120
8. 260
9. 210
10. 20, 70, 80
11. 7.40
12. 6.20
13. 28 centimetres
14. 40 square centimetres
15. 550g
16. 800g
17. 1350g
18. Angle d
19. Angle e
20. c, b, a, d, e
21.

22. V
23. X
24. M
25. A
26. 4
27. 141
28. 61 – 36 = 25
29. 68 – 16 = 52
30. 72 – 57 = 15
31–34.
35. 39
36. 62

37. 44
38. 48
39. 147, 152
40. 195, 197
41. 176, 179
42. 164, 168
43. 186
44. 544
45. 322
46. 8.5cm
47. 4cm
48. 6.5cm
49. 500ml
50. 1250ml

PAPER 2
1. 84
2. 43
3. 25, 34, 36
4. 34, 48, 18
5–10. $\frac{1}{6}, \frac{1}{4}, \frac{1}{3}, \frac{1}{2}, \frac{2}{3}, \frac{3}{4}$,
11. 30 minutes
12. 45 minutes
13. 90 minutes
14. 115 minutes
15–22.

x	7	9	8
5	35	45	40
6	42	54	48

x	3	5	7
10	30	50	70
4	12	20	28

23. 2kg
24. 5000g
25. 4.5kg
26. 6500g
27. 1547
28. 9061
29. 2348
30. TV
31. 14
32. computer and TV
33. reading
34. 52
35. 355
36. 410
37. 516
38. cuboids
39. pyramid
40. cylinders
41. cone
42. cubes
43. sphere
44. 40°C, 27°C, –4°C, –12°C
45–46. $\frac{3}{10}, \frac{2}{5}$
47. 9m
48. 60p
49. £3.90
50. £7.00

PAPER 3
1. 39 + 56 or 59 +36 =95
2. 55p, £1.02
3. $\frac{1}{6}$
4. $\frac{1}{4}$
5. $\frac{1}{8}$
6. $\frac{1}{3}$
7. $\frac{1}{5}$
8. $\frac{1}{8}, \frac{1}{6}, \frac{1}{5}, \frac{1}{4}, \frac{1}{3}$

9–13.

Boys			Girls	
Name	Age		Name	Age
Daniel	10		Jo	10
Ryan	9		Beth	9
James	10		Leanne	10

14. 19
15. 59
16. 38
17. 73
18. >
19. <
20. <
21. >
22. 21 days
23. 2 hours
24. 180 minutes
25. 10 weeks
26. 28 days
27. 240 minutes
28–31. 473, 485, 499, 511
32. 18, 54, 48, 42
33. d) 7000
34. 9
35. 21
36. 80
37. 60
38. 4.40
39. 4
40. 2
41. c) 9 squares
42. 676+32=708
43. 72+49=121
44. 87+54=141
45. c)
46. $\frac{1}{2}$ litre
47. 6kg
48. 14
49. 60
50. 90

PAPER 4
1. c) 301
2–7. 3 x 4 =12, 2 x 5 = 10,
    5 x 8 = 40
8. £470
9. 30
10. 31
11. 33
12. 445
13. 865
14. 1024
15. yes
16. <
17. >
18. <
19. 3.25
20. 2.50

1

21. 11.10
22. 7.05
23. 6 square faces
24. 2 circle faces, 1 curved face
25. 2 square faces, 4 rectangle faces
26. 1 square face, 4 triangle faces
27. 850ml
28. 450ml
29. 250ml
30. 750ml
31. £216
32–34. Check beads make each number.
35. 6 squares
36. 8 squares
37. 10 squares
38. 13 squares
39. 11 squares
40. 7 squares
41. 542
42. 561
43. 514
44. $\frac{3}{9}$
45. $\frac{2}{12}$
46. $\frac{3}{30}$
47–50.

Start position, facing:	Turn	End position, now facing:
Home	$\frac{1}{4}$ turn clockwise	School
Bus station	$\frac{1}{2}$ turn clockwise	Home
Shop	$\frac{1}{4}$ turn anticlockwise	Bus station
School	$\frac{1}{4}$ turn clockwise	Bus station

PAPER 5
1. 205
2. 14
3. $2\frac{1}{2}$, $1\frac{1}{2}$
4–9.

	Symmetrical	Not symmetrical
Triangle	A F	C
Not a triangle	B E	D

10. isosceles triangle
11. rectangle or quadrilateral
12. right-angled triangle
13. trapezium or quadrilateral
14. pentagon
15. equilateral triangle
16. 12
17–22. Check that the angles are correct.
23. 50
24. 42
25. 36
26. 45
27–28. 39 x 4 and 29 x 5 or 39 x 5 and 29 x 4
29. 35 minutes

30. 45 minutes
31. 40 minutes
32. 3 hours 25 minutes
33–37. 81, 18, 45, 56, 72, 36
38. 12
39. 3
40. March
41. 21
42–47.

48. 32cm
49. 20cm
50. 27cm

PAPER 6
1. 9010
2. 9910
3. 9100
4. 9991
5. 1623
6. 386
7. 5094
8. 2474
9–10. 5950, 6050
11–12. 1453, 1463
13–14. 7029. 8029
15. yes
16. 8.20pm
17. 76
18. 78
19. 210
20. 285
21. 28
22. 13
23. 15
24. 38
25–28.

29–36.

Shape	Name	Faces
	Cuboid	
	Pyramid	
	Prism	
	Pyramid or tetrahedron	

37. 8
38. 7
39. 15
40. 3000m
41. 8m
42. 7km
43. 800cm
44. 7.5m
45. 3500m
46. Parcel 1 → 4kg
Parcel 2 → 2kg
Parcel 3 → 5kg
47–48. Check each shape is a rectangle and that one has an area of 18 squares and the other 20 squares.
49. $\frac{2}{4}$
50. $\frac{2}{8}$

PAPER 7
1. 3473
2. 3485
3. 3499
4. 3511
5. 3517
6. $\frac{4}{20}$
7. $\frac{3}{16}$
8. $\frac{3}{4}$
9. 850
10. 1050
11. 220
12. 520
13. 1040
14. 1045
15. 1610
16. 1910
17. 5.05pm
18. 9.15am
19. 11.30am
20. 4.35pm
21. 55
22. Friday
23. 40
24. 75
25. 18
26. 4
27. 3
28. 6
29. 5
30–34.

Start position	Turn	End position
A	$\frac{1}{4}$ turn anticlockwise	D
C	$\frac{3}{4}$ turn clockwise	B
B	$\frac{1}{4}$ turn anticlockwise	A
A	$\frac{1}{4}$ turn clockwise	B
D	$\frac{1}{2}$ turn anticlockwise	B

35. Set A → equilateral triangles
36. Set B → right angled triangles
37. Set C → isosceles triangles

38–43.

Angle	38	39	40	41	42	43
Acute	✓			✓		
Obtuse		✓				✓
Right-angled			✓		✓	

44. <
45. =
46. >
47. <
48. 6500g
49. $4\frac{1}{4}$kg or 4.25kg
50. $\frac{3}{4}$kg or 0.75kg

PAPER 8
1. 8925
2. 6479
3. 4834
4. 9561

5–12.

	Round to the nearest 10	Round to the nearest 100
4148 →	4150	4100
3691 →	3690	3700
6037 →	6040	6000
5689 →	5690	5700

13. 682
14. 303km
15. 1157
16. £1067
17. 683 − 518 = 165
18. 829 − 434 = 395
19. 303km
20. 2523km
21. Amazon and Mississippi
22. 204km
23. Congo
24. Mississippi and Chang Jiang
25. prism
26. pyramid or tetrahedon
27. cube
28. pyramid
29. cuboid

30–34.

	Symmetrical	Not symmetrical
Triangle	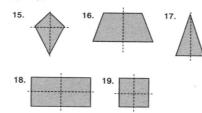	
Not a Triangle		

35. 7
36. 6
37. 146cm
38. 147cm
39. triangle
40. 30m²

41. 14m²
42. 45m²
43. 32m²
44. 10.05pm
45. one of: 15, 51, 61, 65, 81, 85
46. one of: 16, 56
47. one of : 16, 81
48. c) 70%
49. 9,3,6,2
50. 14:25

PAPER 9
1. 8102   8201   <u>8211</u>   (8101)
2. 5956   5965   (5955)   <u>5966</u>
3. (4080)   4089   <u>8064</u>   4803
4. 3
5. 8
6. 9
7. 9
8. 6
9. 8
10. 9.35am
11. Bus C
12. Bus A
13. 40 minutes
14. Bus D

15–19.

15. **16.** **17.**

18. **19.**

20–31.

Shape	Name	Faces	Edges	Vertices
	Tetrahedron	4	6	4
	Cuboid	6	12	8
	Triangular prism	5	9	6
	Square based pyramid	5	8	5

32. 7
33. 9
34. 4
35. 6
36. 54 litres
37. 77cm
38. 90kg
39. 45kg
40. 63cm
41. 125
42. £15
43. 125

44.

45. 25cm
46. 46cm
47. 32cm
48. 37cm
49. 600ml bottle has 300ml of juice, which is more than the 1l bottle.
50. £16.25

PAPER 10
1. $\frac{1}{8}$
2. $\frac{1}{2}$
3. $\frac{3}{4}$
4. $\frac{1}{6}$
5. $\frac{1}{3}$
6. $\frac{5}{6}$
7. 8kg
8. 9000g
9. 3.5kg or $3\frac{1}{2}$kg
10. 2500g
11. 250g
12. 1.75kg or $1\frac{3}{4}$kg
13. 11
14. 148
15. 168
16. 445
17. 444
18. 27cm²
19. 24cm
20. 56cm²
21. 30cm
22. 66cm²
23. 34cm
24. 4 hours 40 minutes
25. 1 hour 15 minutes
26. 11.50am
27. 4.45pm
28. 1900, 2000, 2200
29. 506, 500, 498
30. 3250, 3255, 3260
31. 2100, 2150, 2300
32. 9885
33. 8975
34. 3898
35. 7513
36. 794 − 281 = 513
37. 848 − 615 = 233

38–40.

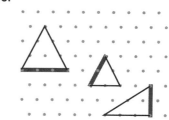

41–45.

Angle	41.	42.	43.	44.	45.
Acute		✓		✓	
Obtuse	✓		✓		
Right-angled					✓

46. b) 1m 62cm
47. 3 sections red; or 2 sections red, 1 section green or blue; or 1 section red, 2 sections green.
48. 350 metres
49. 29 minutes
50. 10 minutes

PAPER 11
1. 34
2. 29
3. 32
4. 33
5. 37
6. 21
7. 9
8. 20
9. no
10. Check scales read 7.5kg.
11. Check scales read 10.75kg.
12. Check scales read 5.25kg.
13. Check scales read 15.75kg.
14. $\frac{2}{4} = \frac{1}{2}$
15. $\frac{2}{6} = \frac{1}{3}$
16. $\frac{6}{8} = \frac{3}{4}$
17. $\frac{4}{6} = \frac{2}{3}$
18. $=$
19. 2.40pm
20. 250g
21. 45°
22. 200
23. 9kg
24. £8
25. £14
26. 15m
27. 18 l
28. 10kg
29. week 3
30. 18
31. week 1
32. week 1
33. 6
34. week 5
35. 24mm
36. 57mm
37. $\frac{1}{2} = \frac{2}{4} = \frac{3}{6} = \frac{4}{8} = \frac{5}{10}$
38. $\frac{2}{3} = \frac{4}{6} = \frac{6}{9} = \frac{8}{12} = \frac{10}{15}$
39. $\frac{3}{4} = \frac{6}{8} = \frac{9}{12} = \frac{12}{15} = \frac{15}{20}$
40. 4
41. 9 or 11
42. 7
43. 9 or 11
44. 9 or 11
45. 9 or 11

46–50.

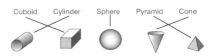

Cuboid   Cylinder   Sphere   Pyramid   Cone

PAPER 12
1. 5973
2. 5985
3. 5999
4. 6002
5. 6017
6. 134
7. 1375
8. 174
9. 27
10. 1133
11. 1477
12. 3.47
13. 2.52
14. 11.38
15. 9.06

16–21.

	Symmetrical	Not symmetrical
Some right-angles	B	C
No right-angles	A E	D

22. 7 squares
23. 9 squares
24. 11 squares
25. 8kg
26. 6.5m
27. 7800g
28. 8500ml
29. 9.2km
30. 5500m
31. 3091
32. 5662
33. 4105
34. 1301
35. 1141
36. 1444
37. 1121
38. £42
39. £152
40. £210
41. £216
42. 1064, 1066
43. 7462, 7464
44. 8372, 8376
45. 58 r 6
46. 84 r 2
47. 122 r 2
48. 102 r 2
49. pyramid or tetrahedron
50. triangular prism.

PAPER 13
1. c) 18
2. 18
3. 5, 15, 3, 9

4. $\frac{1}{3}$ of 45 ➜ 15
5. $\frac{1}{5}$ of 90 ➜ 18
6. $\frac{1}{6}$ of 72 ➜ 12
7. 5
8. 15
9. 5
10. 21 or 15
11. 21
12. 5
13. 92
14. 2000m
15. 6.5m
16. 9km
17. 50cm
18. 45 square metres
19. 42 square metres
20. 6 square metres
21. 15 square metres
22. 28
23. 36
24. 39
25. 45
26. 54

27–29.

31.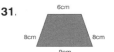

32. $\frac{y}{10}$
33. $\frac{4}{6}$
34. $\frac{6}{15}$
35. $\frac{9}{12}$
36. 100g
37. £2.50
38. 18 litres
39. 8m
40. £60
41. 20kg
42. $\frac{1}{2}$kg
43. 8
44. 43 x 5
45. 15
46. Class 2
47. Class 3
48. 27
49. 15
50. 9

PAPER 14
1. 7490
2. 5163
3. 4057

4. 3866
5. 1677
6. 1204
7. 3817
8. 3929
9. 17cm
10. 23cm
11. 49cm
12. 12cm
13–14. 7044, 7046
15–16. 2962, 2964
17–18. 8172, 8176
19. 548 + 218 = 766
20. 593 + 158 = 751
21. 3.47
22. 6.58
23. 11.31
24. 9.09
25. 1.16
26. 54
27. 127 r 2
28. 128 r 4
29. 96 r 2
30–45.

Shape	Name	Faces	Edges	Vertices
	Square-based pyramid	5	8	5
	Prism	5	9	6
	Cuboid	6	12	8
	tetrahedron	4	6	4

46. Check rectangle is 6cm x 8cm.
47. $\frac{3}{9}$
48. $\frac{2}{10}$
49. 7000
50. 4300

PAPER 15
1. $\frac{1}{10}$
2. $\frac{1}{2}$
3. $\frac{7}{10}$
4. $\frac{2}{5}$
5. $\frac{1}{2}$
6. $\frac{9}{10}$
7. $\frac{1}{4}$
8. $\frac{5}{8}$
9. $\frac{7}{8}$
10. nine thousand six hundred and forty
11. 5
12. 48
13. 4
14. 60
15. 9
16. 24
17. 12
18. 36

19. 8
20. 28
21–24.

	Greater than $\frac{1}{2}$	Less than $\frac{1}{2}$
0.45		✓
0.09		✓
0.7	✓	
0.11		✓

25. 30%
26. 5, 10, 25, 50
27. 36
28. 40p
29–30. 99 ÷ 4, 75 ÷ 8, 66 ÷ 9
31. 28cm²
32. 19.5cm²
33. 7.5cm²
34. 13.5cm²
35–38. 3000g and 4kg → 12kg
8000g and 12kg → 17kg
11kg and 6000g → 20kg
7kg and 5000g → 7kg
39. 18:02
40. 48 weeks
41. cube
42. tetrahedron
43. cuboid
44. prism
45. square based pyramid
46–50.

	Some right-angles	No right-angles
Symmetrical	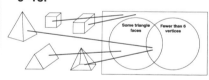	
Not symmetrical		

PAPER 16
1. False
2. True
3. False
4. True
5. 34cm²
6. 9.1
7. 789
8. 758
9. 250 r 3
10. 1190
11. cube
12. triangular prism
13. cuboid
14. tetrahedron
15–22.

Angle	15.	16.	17.	18.	19.	20.	21.	22.
Acute	✓		✓				✓	
Obtuse		✓				✓		
Reflex				✓				✓
Right-angled			✓					

23–26. $\frac{2}{24} = \frac{3}{36} = \frac{4}{48} = \frac{5}{60}$
27–30. $\frac{4}{10} = \frac{6}{15} = \frac{8}{20} = \frac{10}{25}$
31–34. $\frac{6}{16} = \frac{9}{24} = \frac{12}{32} = \frac{15}{40}$
35. 80
36. 53
37. 117
38.

39. Wednesday
40. 17
41. 5
42. Saturday
43. 95
44. 14
45. 60
46. 6
47. 27
48. 18
49. 18
50. 256

PAPER 17
1. $3\frac{1}{4}$
2. $3\frac{3}{8}$
3. $4\frac{1}{2}$
4. $4\frac{3}{4}$
5. 5cm
6. 7cm
7. 2cm
8. 10cm
9–13.

14. $\frac{4}{5}$
15. $\frac{1}{4}$
16. $\frac{1}{100}$
17. $\frac{3}{5}$
18. $\frac{7}{100}$
19. $\frac{3}{4}$
20. 8
21. 8
22. 19
23. 9
24. 57° (accept 56–58°)
25. 19:45
26. 120.1
27. 13.22
28. 22.8
29. 5.05
30–32. (9,8) (4,3) (10, 9)
33. 21
34. 12
35. 8
36. 3
37. 0

38. 4
39. 9 or 11
40. 4
41. 11
42. 40mm, 4.5cm, 20cm, $\frac{1}{4}$ m
43. 250ml
44. 550ml
45. 20cm
46. Example of completed artwork:

47. b) 1 in 4
48. 70%
49. 25%
50. 30%

PAPER 18

1. b) $6\frac{9}{100}$
2–7. $\frac{3}{9} = \frac{1}{3}$, $\frac{1}{4} = \frac{2}{8}$, $\frac{2}{3} = \frac{8}{12}$
8. 8 → eight 375ml
9. 400 920
10. 899 179
11. 102 034
12. 517 000
13. shape c)
14. 8413 – 5425
15. 23
16. 5
17. 24
18. 21
19. 27
20. 63
21. 8
22. 6
23. 21
24. 45mm
25. 53mm
26. 28mm
27. c) 60
28. 88 r 1
29. 61 r 4
30. 75 r 1
31. 77
32–33. 1600g = 1.6kg
34–35. 800g = 0.8kg
36–37. 1700g = 1.7kg
38–39. 2800g = 2.8kg
40. 80°
41. 90°
42. 50°
43. 720
44. 912km
45. 2380g
46. 1280
47. 25
48. 64
49. 81
50. 36

PAPER 19

1. c) 8.15
2–6.

Take-off time	Flying time	Landing time
09:45	2 hr 25 mins	12:10
10:30	1 hr 40 mins	12:10
11:55	1 hr 15 mins	13:10
12:40	2 hr 35 mins	15:15
13:10	1 hr 25 mins	14:35

7. 1481 + 5894 = 7375
8. 4387 + 1495 = 5882
9. 2568 + 5257 = 7825
10. 2
11. 147
12. 36cm^2
13. 26cm
14. $\frac{3}{5}$
15. 60%
16. $\frac{2}{5}$
17. 40%
18. 35
19. 0.3
20. 0.46
21. 0.6
22. 0.73
23. 0.93
24–29.

	A	B	C	D	E	F
Prism	✓	✓				✓
Pyramid			✓	✓	✓	

30. 22 – (12 – 5)
31. 16 – (10 – 9)
32. 25 – (5 + 5)
33. (6 + 13) – 4 or 6 + (13 – 4)
34. (27 – 6) – 6
35. 23 – (10 – 2)
36. b) $\frac{7}{8}$
37. 8 → (1, 8) (2, 4)
38. 20 → (1, 20) (2, 10) (4, 5)
39. 12 → (1, 12) (2, 6) (3,4)
40–43. Approx. 16kg,
Actual 16.54kg
Approx. 21kg,
Actual 20.86kg
44. $\frac{2}{3} = \frac{4}{6} = \frac{6}{9} = \frac{8}{12}$
45. $\frac{3}{4} = \frac{6}{8} = \frac{9}{12} = \frac{12}{15}$
46. $\frac{4}{5} = \frac{8}{10} = \frac{12}{15} = \frac{16}{20}$
47. 780, 425
48. 425
49. 780, 762
50. 116, 425

PAPER 20

1. 24
2. 15
3. 46
4. 18
5. 6
6. 39
7–12. 12cm^2, 16cm, 15cm^2, 16cm 12cm^2, 14cm
13. >
14. <
15. <
16. <
17. c) 18.46
18. Clock a)
19. 19, 18, 18, 18, 17, 17, 16, 15, 15
20. 17
21. 18
22. 3
23. 17
24. 4
25. 1250ml
26. 6.17
27. 6.3
28. 6.56
29. 6.78
30. 6.89
31. 7
32. 9
33. 78
34. 0
35. 936
36. 2795
37. 2924
38. square-based pyramid
39. tetrahedron
40. triangular prism
41. cuboid
42. $\frac{9}{10}$
43. $\frac{4}{10}$
44. $\frac{6}{18}$
45. $\frac{3}{15}$
46. $\frac{1}{5}$
47. $\frac{9}{12}$
48. 330ml, 0.5 litres, 700ml, 3.3 litres, 5000ml, 7 litres
49. 80g, 0.8kg, 880g, 1.8kg, 8kg, 8100g
50. 4738 + 9163 = 13901

PAPER 21
1. 2
2. 65
3. 266 r 2
4. 16
5. 64
6. 144
7. c)
8–9. 36, 24
10. 19cm²
11. 24cm
12. 171cm²
13. 60cm
14. 336cm²
15. 84cm
16. c)
17–30.

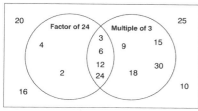

30. 3
31. 2
32. 9
33. 7
34. 3
35. 6
37. 24 → (1, 24) (2, 12), (3, 8) (4, 6)
38. 28 → (1,28) (2, 14) (4, 7)
39. 30 → (1, 30) (2, 15) (3, 10) (5, 6)
40–41. 2200ml = 2.2 litres
42–43. 800ml = 0.8 litres
44–45. 1400ml = 1.4 litres
46–47. 2600ml = 2.6 litres
48. 1
49. 2
50. 3

PAPER 22
1. 1053
2. 4964
3. 1764
4. 4032
5. $\frac{1}{100}$
6. $3\frac{2}{10}$ or $3\frac{1}{5}$
7. $7\frac{1}{8}$
8. $\frac{18}{100}$ or $\frac{9}{50}$
9. $\frac{9}{10}$
10. $\frac{3}{10}$
11. $\frac{7}{100}$
12. $2\frac{4}{10}$ or $2\frac{2}{5}$
13. a) 14
14. d) 16
15. $\frac{1}{4}, \frac{3}{8}, \frac{1}{2}, \frac{10}{16}$
16. $\frac{1}{6}, \frac{1}{3}, \frac{6}{12}, \frac{3}{4}$
17. $\frac{5}{15}, \frac{1}{2}, \frac{3}{5}, \frac{2}{3}$
18. $\frac{4}{20}, \frac{1}{2}, \frac{7}{10}, \frac{4}{5}$
19. 18.2
20. 18.45
21. 18.69
22. 18.78
23. 18.92
24. c) $\frac{3}{4}$
25. 1.2 litres
26. 6500ml
27. 1 litre
28. 4000ml
29. 39.02
30. 17.23
31. 40.76
32. 19.78
33–37.

Triangle	A	B	C	D	E
Scalene	✓				✓
Equilateral			✓		
Isosceles		✓		✓	
Right-angled	✓			✓	

38. 257cm²
39. 72cm
40. 300cm²
41. 110cm
42. 480cm²
43. 128cm
44. b) 45
45. 1 kg 250g or 1$\frac{1}{2}$kg or 1.25kg
46. 21:05
47. 147 r 1
48. 89
49. 177 r 1
50. 67 r 4

PAPER 23
1. a) 7
2. 12cm
3. mean
4. 3
5. 2750g
6. 5.5kg
7. 3kg
8. 4kg
9. 390
10. 100
11. 85.77
12. 10
13. 1900
14. 100
15. 1830
16. 10
17. >
18. >
19. b) $\frac{3}{4}$
20. 972
21. 414m
22. 1128
23. 5600g or 5.6kg
24. $\frac{1}{5}$
25. $\frac{1}{10}$
26. $\frac{1}{2}$
27. $\frac{4}{5}$
28. $\frac{1}{4}$
29. $\frac{3}{4}$
30. 520
31. 1080
32. 1760
33. 2800
34. 3440
35. 3 and 5
36. 2, 3, 4 and 6
37. 2 and 4
38. 2, 3, 4, 6 and 9
39. 52 weeks and 2 days
40. 9
41. 69
42. 23
43. 300 945
44. 89 409
45. 202 035
46. 517 261
47–50.

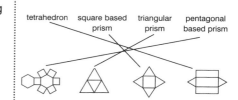

PAPER 24

1. 3
2. 10
3. c) 81
4. $2\frac{1}{4}$
5. $5\frac{2}{3}$
6. $1\frac{1}{6}$
7. $9\frac{1}{2}$
8. $\frac{16}{5}$
9. $\frac{19}{8}$
10. $\frac{11}{2}$
11. $\frac{27}{4}$
12. >
13. >
14. <
15. >
16. 9570
17. 11 803
18. 15 479
19. 12
20. 18

21. 3
22. 40
23. £56
24. £17
25. £18
26. £50
27. £242
28. £309
29. 61mm
30. 32mm
31. 29mm
32. c) 72
33. 2, 4, 64, 128
34. 2.5, 5, 80, 160
35. 1.82m, 1.79m, 1.7m,1.68m
36. 87.37kg, 87.12kg, 80.29kg, 78.61kg
37. 13°
38. 21°
39. 33°
40. angle d)

41. 5n
42. 3n+1
43. 12 → 1, 2, 3, 4, 6, 12
44. 27 → 1, 3, 9, 27
45. 45 → 1, 3, 5, 9, 15, 45
46. 36 → 1, 2, 3, 4, 6, 9, 12, 18, 36
47. c) 5.40pm
48.

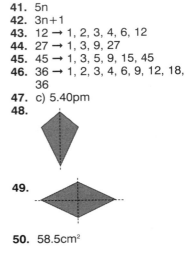

49.

50. 58.5cm²

12–15. Write the times shown on these clocks.

_____   _____   _____   _____   /4

16–21. Write the letter for each shape on the diagram.

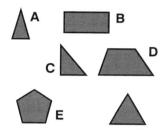

	Symmetrical	Not symmetrical
Some right-angles		
No right-angles		

/6

22–24. What is the approximate area of these shapes?

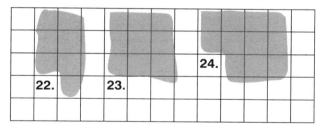

22. _____ squares

23. _____ squares

24. _____ squares   /3

25–30. Complete these.

8000g = ☐ kg   650cm = ☐ m   7.8kg = ☐ g

8 ½ litres = ☐ ml   9200m = ☐ km   5km 500m = ☐ m   /6

31–33. Write the number shown on each abacus.

/3

Answer these.

34. 812
   + 489
   ____

   ____

35. 346
   + 795
   ____

   ____

36. 635
   + 809
   ____

   ____

37. 724
   + 397
   ____

   ____

/4

38–41. Write the total cost for each of these.

£14

£38

£42

£36

3 footballs _____   4 rackets _____   5 pairs _____   6 pairs _____

/4

Look at these number patterns. Write the next two numbers.

42.   1054   1056   1058   1060   1062   _____   _____

43.   7452   7454   7456   7458   7460   _____   _____

44.   8352   8356   8360   8364   8368   _____   _____

/3

45–48. Complete these.

9)‾528‾   8)‾674‾   7)‾856‾   6)‾614‾

/4

49–50. Name each of these shapes from the nets.

   Name:
   _____

   Name:
   _____

/2

/50

PAPER 13

1. 24 x 18 is more than 23 x 18. How much more? Tick the correct answer.

    a) 24   **b)** 1   **c)** 18   **d)** 23   /1

2. What is the smallest number that is divisible by both six and by nine? _____   /1

3. Put a ring round the numbers that are factors of 45.   4   5   90   15   3   9   12   /1

4–6. Match each of these to the correct answer, by drawing a line.

     $\frac{1}{3}$ of 45 $\frac{1}{5}$ of 90 $\frac{1}{6}$ of 72

     14   22   15   18   16   12   20   /3

7–12. Choose any of the numbers in the box to complete each of these.   **8   5   15   21**

     6 x ☐ < 40   18 − ☐ < 4   40 ÷ ☐ = 8

     ☐ − 7 > 6   ☐ + 21 > 40   ☐ x 4 < 30   /6

13. A school has exactly twice as many boys as girls.
There are 184 boys. How many girls are there? _____   /1

14–17. Complete these.

     2km = ☐ m   650cm = ☐ m   9000m = ☐ km   0.5m = ☐ cm   /4

Calculate the area of these rectangles.

18. 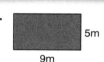 5m   **19.** 6m   **20.** 1.5m   **21.** 2.5m

   9m   7m   4m   6m

Area = _____ m²   Area = _____ m²   Area = _____ m²   Area = _____ m²   /4

22–26. Look at this function machine. Complete the chart for the machine.

IN		51		60	
OUT	13		24		39

   /5

27–30. Draw the total weight on each weighing scale.

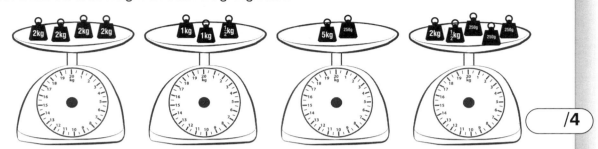

/4

31. Tick the shape that has the greatest perimeter.

9cm 6cm

10cm 10cm 10cm

6cm 8cm 8cm 9cm

6cm 6cm 6cm 6cm 6cm

/1

32–35. Complete these equivalent fractions.

$$\frac{1}{2} = \frac{\square}{10} \qquad \frac{2}{3} = \frac{\square}{6} \qquad \frac{2}{5} = \frac{\square}{15} \qquad \frac{3}{4} = \frac{\square}{12}$$

/4

Answer these.

36. $\frac{1}{3}$ of 300g = _____

37. $\frac{1}{10}$ of £25 = _____

38. $\frac{1}{5}$ of 90 litres = _____

39. $\frac{1}{6}$ of 48m = _____

40. $\frac{1}{4}$ of £240 = _____

41. $\frac{1}{8}$ of 160kg = _____

/6

42. A 2kg bag of flour is used for cooking.
$\frac{3}{4}$ of the flour is used. What weight of flour is left? _____

/1

43. Write the missing digit.

$$\begin{array}{r} 3\,\square \\ \times\quad 7 \\ \hline 266 \\ \hline \end{array}$$

/1

44. Use the digits 3, 4 and 5 once to make the multiplication with the greatest product.

$\square\,\square \times \square$ = _____

/1

45. Here is a number sequence. Write the next number in the sequence.

1   3   6   10 $\square$

/1

This graph shows the total number of days in a year that the children were away from school in each class.

46. Which class had the most children absent during the year? _____

47. Which class had 21 absences through the year? _____

48. How many children were absent from Class 6?
_____

49. How many more children were absent from Class 4 than from Class 5? _____

50. $\frac{1}{4}$ of the days absent in Class 2 were because Alex broke his arm and so he missed some days in school. How many days did he miss? _____

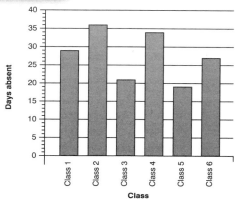

/5

/50

PAPER 14

Write the number shown on each abacus.

1.

2.

3.

4.

/4

Complete these.

5.	930	6.	845	7.	3249	8.	3054
	+ 747		+ 359		+ 568		+ 875

/4

This graph shows the heights of the Jones family.

9. How much taller is Dad than Mum?

_____

10. How much smaller is Jo than her mother?

_____

11. If Sam grows up to be the same height as his father how many more centimetres will he need to grow?

_____

12. What is the difference in height between Rob and Mel?

_____

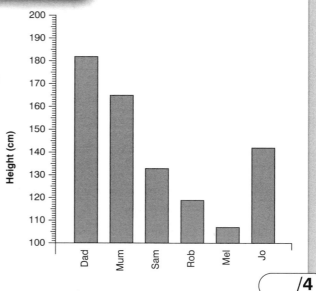

/4

Look at these number patterns. Write the next two numbers.

13–14. 7034   7036   7038   7040   7042   _____   _____

15–16. 2952   2954   2956   2958   2960   _____   _____

17–18. 8152   8156   8160   8164   8168   _____   _____   /6

19–20. Complete these, using each of the digits 1, 2, 3, 4, 5 and 6 once.

$$
\begin{array}{r}
5\ \square\ 8 \\
+\ \square\ 1\ 8 \\
\hline
7\ 6\ \square \\
\end{array}
\qquad
\begin{array}{r}
5\ 9\ \square \\
+\ \square\ 5\ 8 \\
\hline
7\ \square\ 1 \\
\end{array}
$$

/2

21–25. Write the times shown on these clocks.

_____   _____   _____   _____   _____   /5

Complete these.

26. 6⟌324   **27.** 5⟌637   **28.** 7⟌900   **29.** 9⟌866   /4

30–45. Count the edges, faces and vertices on each shape and complete the chart.

Shape	Name	Faces	Edges	Vertices
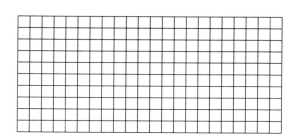				

/16

46. A rectangle has an area of 48 square centimetres and a perimeter of 28cm.

Draw the rectangle on this grid.

/1

Tick the shape that shows an equivalent fraction. Write the equivalent fraction for each.

47. □/□ $\frac{1}{3}$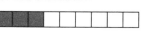

48. □/□ $\frac{1}{5}$ /2

49–50. Round each of these numbers to the nearest 100.

7035 → _____   4252 → _____   /2

/50

PAPER 15

1–9. Write the fraction each arrow is pointing to. Simplify the fractions if needed.

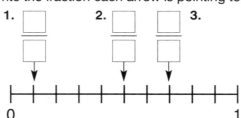
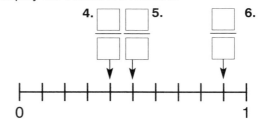

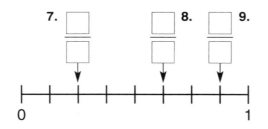

/9

10. Make the largest number possible with the digits 6, 0, 9, and 4. Write your number as a word.

 _____

/1

11–20. Look at these function machines. Complete the chart for each machine.

IN		8		10	
OUT	30		24		54

IN		48		32	
OUT	6		9		7

/10

21–24. Put a tick in each row to complete this.

	Greater than $\frac{1}{2}$	Less than $\frac{1}{2}$
0.45		
0.09		
0.7		
0.11		

/4

25. What is three-tenths as a percentage? _____

/1

26. Put a circle around the numbers that are factors of fifty.

5   10   25   50   100   150

/1

27. The difference between two numbers is 9.
The larger number is 45. What is the other number? _____

/1

28. It costs £1.60 for 4 pies. What is the cost of each pie? _____

/1

29–30. Underline the questions that have an answer with a remainder of 3.

86 ÷ 5   99 ÷ 4   75 ÷ 8   66 ÷ 9

/2

Calculate the area of each rectangle.

31.

32.

33.

34.

3.5cm

3cm

1.5cm

3cm

8cm

6.5cm

5cm

4.5cm

_____   _____   _____   _____

/4

Each of the weighing scales holds 2 boxes. Join the
boxes to the scales in pairs to make the totals.

 7kg

 3000g

8000g

 12kg

 5000g

 4kg

6000g

11kg

35.   **36.**   **37.**   **38.**

/4

39. A train is due in to the station at 17:48, but it is 14 minutes late. At what time will it arrive?

_____

/1

40. How many weeks are there in 336 days? _____

/1

45

Name each of these shapes from the nets.

41.   **42.**   **43.**   **44.**   **45.**

/5

46–50. Draw each shape on the diagram.

	Some right-angles	No right-angles
Symmetrical		
Not symmetrical		

/5

/50

PAPER 16

Write TRUE or FALSE for these.

1. $87 + 54 > 57 + 84$ _____

2. $48 \times 10 > 3.8 \times 100$ _____

3. $108 - 60 < 92 - 48$ _____

4. $340 \div 10 < 3405 \div 100$ _____

/4

5. What is the area of this shape?

_____cm^2

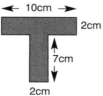

/1

6. Ten times a number is ninety-one. What is the number? _____

/1

Answer these.

7. $5\overline{)3945}$ **8.** $9\overline{)6822}$ **9.** $8\overline{)2003}$ **10.** $6\overline{)7140}$ **/4**

What shapes are these? Name each shape from the list given.

cuboid   cube   triangular prism   tetrahedron

11. I have 6 square faces. What am I? _____

12. I have 2 triangle faces and 3 rectangle faces. What am I? _____

13. I have 2 square faces and 4 rectangle faces. What am I? _____

14. I have 4 triangle faces. What am I? _____   **/4**

15–22. Tick to show whether each angle is acute, obtuse, reflex or right-angled.

Angle	15.	16.	17.	18.	19.	20.	21.	22.
Acute								
Obtuse								
Reflex								
Right-angled								

/8

23–34. Complete these equivalent fraction chains.

$$\frac{1}{12} = \frac{2}{\square} = \frac{\square}{36} = \frac{4}{60} = \frac{\square}{\square}$$

$$\frac{2}{5} = \frac{\square}{10} = \frac{6}{\square} = \frac{\square}{20} = \frac{10}{\square}$$

$$\frac{3}{8} = \frac{6}{\square} = \frac{\square}{24} = \frac{12}{\square} = \frac{\square}{40}$$

/12

35–37. Answer these.

$$4^2 + 8^2 = \square$$

$$7^2 + 2^2 = \square$$

$$9^2 + 6^2 = \square$$

38. Draw the lines of symmetry on this shape.

/4

Mr Ali is a dentist. This graph shows the number of people who visited him as patients each day during a week.

39. On which day did the most people visit Mr Ali?

_____

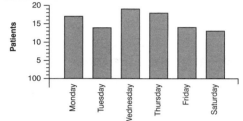

40. How many patients visited him on Monday?

_____

41. How many fewer people visited him on Tuesday than on Wednesday? _____

42. On which day was Mr Ali visited by 13 people? _____

43. How many people visited Mr Ali altogether during this week? _____

/5

Answer these.

44. $\frac{2}{5}$ of 35 = ☐ **45.** $\frac{3}{4}$ of 80= ☐ **46.** $\frac{3}{7}$ of 14= ☐

47. $\frac{9}{10}$ of 30= ☐ **48.** $\frac{3}{8}$ of 48 = ☐ **49.** $\frac{2}{3}$ of 27= ☐

/6

50. A school has eight classes, each with 32 children. How many children are there in school altogether? _____

/1

/50

PAPER 17

1–4. Write the mixed number fraction each arrow is pointing to. Simplify the fractions if needed.

1. ☐ ☐ **2.**   **3.** ☐ **4.** ☐

/4

Calculate the length of each side of these squares.

5. Area = 25cm²
Length of side = _____ cm

6. Area = 49cm²
Length of side = _____ cm

7. Area = 4cm²
Length of side = _____ cm

8. Area = 100cm²
Length of side = _____ cm

/4

9–13. Draw lines to show where each shape belongs on this Venn diagram.

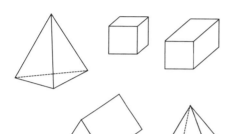
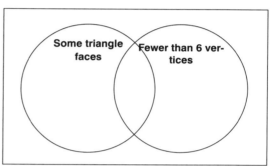

Some triangle faces   Fewer than 6 vertices

/5

14–19. Write the following decimals as fractions in their lowest terms.

0.8 → $\frac{\square}{\square}$ 0.25 → $\frac{\square}{\square}$ 0.01 → $\frac{\square}{\square}$ 0.6 → $\frac{\square}{\square}$ 0.07 → $\frac{\square}{\square}$ 0.75 → $\frac{\square}{\square}$

/6

Write the missing numbers.

20. $(8 \times 4) - (9 + \square) = 15$

21. $(7 + 5) \times (\square - 5) = 36$

22. $(\square - 7) \div (15 - 11) = 3$

23. $(3 \times \square) + (15 - 9) = 33$

/4

24. Measure angle *A* accurately. Use a protractor.

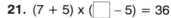

A

25. How would quarter to eight in the evening be shown on a 24-hour digital clock?

:

/2

Answer these.

26. 21.2
     + 98.9
     ‾‾‾‾‾

     ‾‾‾‾‾

27. 5.87
     + 7.35
     ‾‾‾‾‾

     ‾‾‾‾‾

28. 93.5
     − 70.7
     ‾‾‾‾‾

     ‾‾‾‾‾

29. 9.24
     − 4.19
     ‾‾‾‾‾

     ‾‾‾‾‾

/4

30–32. (1,0) and (6,5) are two points on a straight line.

Tick which of these are coordinates
of other points on the line.

(4, 2)   (2, 3)   (9, 8)

(7, 8)   (4, 3)   (10, 9)

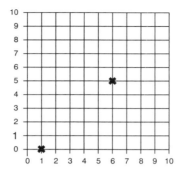

/3

33–37. This is a 'subtract 12' machine. Look at
the chart and write the numbers that enter
the machine.

IN					
OUT	9	0	–4	–9	–12

/5

38–41. Choose any of the numbers in the box to complete each of these. | **4 6 9 11** |

$(6 \times \square) + 3 < 40$ $(16 - 9) \times \square > 60$ $60 \div (\square + 8) = 5$ $(\square - 4) + 6 > 12$

/4

42. Write these lengths in order, starting with the shortest.

$\frac{1}{4}$m   40mm   4.5cm   20cm   _____

/1

43. How much juice is in this jug?

_____

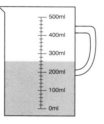

44. How much water must be added to make 800ml of drink?

_____

/2

45. The perimeter of a regular octagon is 160cm. What is the length of each side?

_____

/1

46. Write the missing red and blue sections on this spinner so that you are
equally as likely to spin red as you are to spin blue.

47. On this spinner, what is the likelihood of spinning green?
Tick the correct answer.

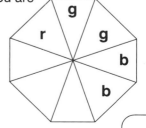

a) 1 in 2   **b)** 1 in 3   **c)** 1 in 4   **d)** 2 in 3

/2

Write the following as percentages.

48. $\dfrac{7}{10}$ = _____   **49.** $\dfrac{5}{20}$ = _____   **50.** $\dfrac{15}{50}$ = _____   /3

/50

PAPER 18

1. What is 6.09 as a fraction? Tick the correct answer.

a) $6\frac{9}{10}$ **b)** $6\frac{9}{100}$ **c)** $6\frac{90}{100}$ **d)** $6\frac{1}{9}$ /1

2–7. The digits **1, 2, 3, 4, 8** and **9** are missing from these equivalent fractions. Write the digits in the correct place.

$\dfrac{3}{\square} = \dfrac{\square}{3}$ $\dfrac{1}{\square} = \dfrac{\square}{8}$ $\dfrac{2}{\square} = \dfrac{\square}{12}$ /6

8. Robert pours a 3 litre jug of apple juice into smaller bottles. He has a supply of bottles in just 3 sizes:

What is the smallest number of bottles he needs to fill to hold exactly 3 litres? _____

0.25ml   375ml   400ml   3 Litres

/1

Read these and write each as a number.

9. four hundred thousand nine hundred and twenty _____

10. eighty-nine thousand one hundred and seventy-nine _____

11. one hundred and two thousand and thirty-four _____

12. five hundred and seventeen thousand _____   /4

13. Which of these is a prism? Tick the correct answer.

a)   b)   c)

 /1

14. The missing digits are **2**, **3**, **4** and **5**. Complete the subtraction.

$$\boxed{8}\ \square\ \boxed{1}\ \square\ -\ \boxed{5}\ \boxed{4}\ \square\ \square\ = \textbf{2988}$$

/1

Answer each of these.

15. $(17 - 3) + 9 = \square$ **16.** $14 - (7 + 2) = \square$ **17.** $(13 - 5) \times 3 = \square$

18. $27 - (9 - 3) = \square$ **19.** $9 \times (7 - 4) = \square$

 /5

What's my number? Work out the mystery number for each of these.

20. When I divide my number by 7 the answer is 9. _____

21. When I multiply my number by 6 the answer is 48. _____

22. When I double my number and then add 5 the answer is 17. _____

23. When I divide my number by 3 and then add 8 the answer is 15. _____

/4

Use a ruler to measure the length of each line accurately in millimetres.

24. ▬▬▬▬▬▬▬▬▬ _____mm

25. ▬▬▬▬▬▬▬▬▬▬ _____mm

26. ▬▬▬▬▬ _____mm

 /3

27. Which of these numbers is a common multiple of 5 and 6? Tick the correct answer.

    a) 12   **b)** 35   **c)** 60   **d)** 40

/1

28–31. Answer these.

$$6\overline{)529} \qquad 8\overline{)492} \qquad 5\overline{)376} \qquad 4\overline{)308}$$

/4

Read these scales and write each weight in grams and kilograms.

32–33.

34–35.

36–37.

38–39.

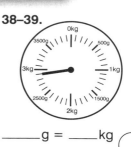

_____g = _____kg   _____g = _____kg   _____g = _____kg   _____g = _____kg

/8

Write the size of the missing angle on each of these shapes.

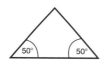

40. _____°   **41.** _____°   **42.** _____°

/3

Read and answer these.

43. There are 24 hours in a day. How many hours are there in April? _____

44. A lorry makes a 76km journey 12 times
in a week. How far did the lorry travel in total? _____

45. A packet of crisps weighs 28g and there are 85 packets
in box. How many grams of crisps are there in a full box? _____

46. There are 64 pages in a book with 20 questions on
each page. How many questions are there in total? _____

/4

Write the next square number in each sequence.

47.   1   4   9   16   _____   **48.**   16   25   36   49   _____

49.   25   36   49   64   _____   **50.**   4   9   16   25   _____

/4

/50

PAPER 19

1. What number is the arrow pointing to? Tick the correct answer.

a) 8.5 **b)** 8.25
c) 8.15 **d)** 8.05

/1

2–6. These are the take-off times for some UK flights from an airport.
For each flight work out the landing time. Write the times using 24-hour time.

Take-off time	Flying time	Landing time
09:45	2 hr 25 mins	
10:30	1 hr 40 mins	
11:55	1 hr 15 mins	
12:40	2 hr 35 mins	
13:10	1 hr 25 mins	

/5

7–9. The digits 4 and 5 are missing from these additions. Complete them with the digits in the correct place.

```
    1 □ 8 1          □ 3 8 7          2 □ 6 8
+     □ 8 9 □     +  1 □ 9 5     +    □ 2 □ 7
  ─────────          ─────────        ─────────
    7 3 7 □          □ 8 8 2          7 8 2 □
  ─────────          ─────────        ─────────
```

/3

10. How many lines of symmetry has this shape?

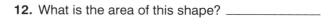 _____

/1

11. Stuart has a set of books that he wants to count. He knows that he has between 120 and 150 books, but not the exact number. He decides to count them in fives, and he has 2 left over. He then counts them in sixes and he has 3 left over.

How many books has Stuart got? _____

/1

12. What is the area of this shape? _____

13. What is the perimeter of the shape? _____

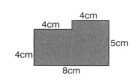

/2

50 children went on a school trip, 20 girls and 30 boys.

14. What fraction are boys? _____

15. What percentage are boys? _____

16. What fraction are girls? _____

17. What percentage are girls? _____

18. $\frac{3}{10}$ of the group of children are under 8 years old. How many children are 8 years or older? _____

/5

19–23. Write the decimal number each arrow points to.

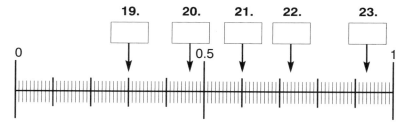

19. **20.** **21.** **22.** **23.**

/5

24–29. Sort these shapes into prisms and pyramids. Complete this table by ticking the boxes.

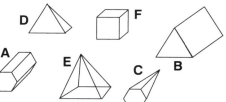

	A	B	C	D	E	F
Prism						
Pyramid						

/6

30–35. Write brackets to make each answer 15.

30. 22 – 12 – 5

31. 16 – 10 – 9

32. 25 – 5 + 5

33. 6 + 13 – 4

34. 27 – 6 – 6

35. 23 – 10 – 2

/6

36. Which of these fractions is greater than $\frac{3}{4}$?

   a) $\frac{7}{12}$ **b)** $\frac{7}{8}$ **c)** $\frac{3}{5}$ **d)** $\frac{3}{8}$

/1

37–39. Write all the pairs of factors for each of these.

8

(☐ , ☐)
(☐ , ☐)

20

(☐ , ☐)
(☐ , ☐)
(☐ , ☐)

12

(☐ , ☐)
(☐ , ☐)
(☐ , ☐)

/3

40–43. Round each of these to the nearest whole number of kilograms. Write the approximate total weights for each set. Calculate the actual total weight for each set.

4.38kg   2.97kg   9.19kg

Approx. total weight _____kg

Actual total weight _____kg

9.49kg   7.73kg   3.64kg

Approx. total weight _____kg

Actual total weight _____kg

/4

Complete these equivalent fraction chains.

44. $\dfrac{2}{3} = \dfrac{4}{\Box} = \dfrac{\Box}{9} = \dfrac{\Box}{\Box}$

45. $\dfrac{3}{4} = \dfrac{\Box}{8} = \dfrac{9}{\Box} = \dfrac{\Box}{\Box}$

46. $\dfrac{4}{5} = \dfrac{8}{\Box} = \dfrac{\Box}{15} = \dfrac{\Box}{\Box}$

/3

Use these numbers to answer the problems.

116   667   780   425   762

47. Which numbers are exactly divisible by 5? _____

48. Which of the numbers has a remainder of 1 when the divisor is 4? _____

49. Which of the numbers have 6 as a factor? _____

50. Which of the numbers has a remainder of 2 when the divisor is 3? _____

/4

/50

PAPER 20

Circle the number in each set that is **not** a square number.

1.	36	24	16	64

2.	25	81	9	15

3.	1	100	46	4

4.	18	49	9	81

5.	16	6	4	64

6.	49	9	39	100

/6

7–12. Use a ruler to measure the sides of these shapes in centimetres. Write the area and perimeter for each shape.

area = _____cm²

perimeter = _____cm

area = _____cm²

perimeter = _____cm

area = _____cm²

perimeter = _____cm

/6

Write < , > or = between each pair of fractions.

13. $\frac{2}{3}$ ☐ $\frac{1}{2}$ **14.** $\frac{1}{4}$ ☐ $\frac{1}{3}$ **15.** $\frac{2}{3}$ ☐ $\frac{4}{5}$ **16.** $\frac{1}{2}$ ☐ $\frac{3}{4}$

/4

17. Which number would round to 18 as its nearest whole number?

    a) 17.47   **b)** 18.73   **c)** 18.46   **d)** 17.09

/1

18. Tick the clock that shows 23.25.

a)   **b)**   **c)**    **d)**

/1

Levels 4/5

These are the results of a spelling test for a group of nine children.

(18) (16) (17) (17) (18) (15) (15) (18) (19)

19. Write the scores in order, starting with the highest.

_____

20. What is the median score? _____

21. Which score is the mode? _____

22. How many scores are in the mode group? _____

23. Calculate the mean score. _____

24. How many children got more than the mean average score? _____

/6

25. What is the amount of water shown in this jug? _____ml

/1

26–30. Write the decimal number each arrow points to.

26. **27.** **28.** **29.** **30.**

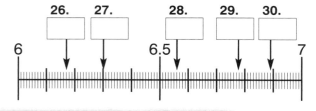

/5

Write the answer for each of these.

31. $(8 + 6) \div 2 = \boxed{}$ **32.** $(18 + 12) - (13 + 8) = \boxed{}$

33. $(9 \times 7) + (3 \times 5) = \boxed{}$ **34.** $(35 - 19) + (43 - 27) = \boxed{}$

/4

Answer these.

35. 39
      x 24
      ‾‾‾

      ‾‾‾

36. 43
      x 65
      ‾‾‾

      ‾‾‾

37. 68
      x 43
      ‾‾‾

      ‾‾‾

/3

Write the name of the shape described in each of these.

38. Which shape has 5 faces, 8 edges and 5 vertices? _____

39. Which shape has 4 faces, 6 edges and 4 vertices? _____

40. Which shape has 5 faces, 9 edges and 6 vertices? _____

41. Which shape has 6 faces, 12 edges and 8 vertices? _____   /4

These are sets of equivalent fractions.
Cross out the odd one in each set.

42. $\dfrac{9}{10}$ $\dfrac{4}{5}$ $\dfrac{16}{20}$ $\dfrac{8}{10}$ $\dfrac{12}{15}$ **43.** $\dfrac{4}{20}$ $\dfrac{3}{15}$ $\dfrac{5}{25}$ $\dfrac{4}{10}$ $\dfrac{1}{5}$

44. $\dfrac{3}{6}$ $\dfrac{6}{12}$ $\dfrac{8}{16}$ $\dfrac{6}{18}$ $\dfrac{1}{2}$ **45.** $\dfrac{5}{15}$ $\dfrac{3}{15}$ $\dfrac{3}{9}$ $\dfrac{1}{3}$ $\dfrac{9}{27}$

46. $\dfrac{6}{24}$ $\dfrac{5}{20}$ $\dfrac{1}{5}$ $\dfrac{4}{16}$ $\dfrac{1}{4}$ **47.** $\dfrac{2}{3}$ $\dfrac{6}{9}$ $\dfrac{9}{12}$ $\dfrac{10}{15}$ $\dfrac{12}{18}$ /6

Write each set in order starting with the smallest.

48. 700ml   3.3 litres   5000ml   0.5 litres   7 litres   330ml

_____

49. 1.8kg   80g   880g   0.8kg   8kg   80g

_____   /2

50. All the digits 1 and 3 are missing. Write the digits 1   /1
or 3 in the correct place to complete this addition.

$$
\begin{array}{r}
4\ 7\ \square\ 8 \\
+\ \ 9\ \square\ 6\ \square \\
\hline
\square\ \square\ 9\ 0\ \square \\
\hline
\end{array}
$$

/50

PAPER 21

Answer these.

1. What is the remainder when 974 is divided by 4? _____

2. Divide 520 by 8. _____

3. What is the remainder when 800 is divided by 3? _____

/3

Write the next square number in each sequence.

4.   1   4   9 _____   **5.**   25   36   49 _____

6.   81   100   121 _____

/3

7. Tick the shape that has 6 vertices.

   a)   **b)**   **c)**   **d)**

/1

8–9. Which two numbers between 20 and 40 are common multiples of 3 and 4?

_____   _____

/2

10–15. Calculate the area and perimeter of each of these shapes.

   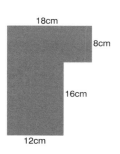

/6

   Area = _____cm²   Area = _____cm²   Area = _____cm²

   Perimeter = _____cm   Perimeter = _____cm   Perimeter = _____cm

16. Which angle is approximately 100°? _____

   a)   **b)**   **c)**   **d)**

/1

17–30. Write these numbers in the correct part of the Venn diagram.

12	4	6	25
18	10	24	16
15	3	20	9
2	30		

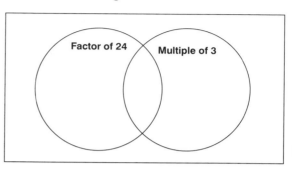

/14

Write the missing numbers.

31. (☐ x 4) − 5 = 7

32. 20 − (☐ x 3) = 14

33. (4 x 2) + (☐ x 3) = 35

34. (☐ x 5) − (5 x 4) = 15

35. 24 ÷ (☐ x 2) = 4

36. (☐ x 5) ÷ 3 = 10

/6

37–39. Write all the pairs of factors for each of these numbers.

24	28	30
(☐,☐)	(☐,☐)	(☐,☐)
(☐,☐)	(☐,☐)	(☐,☐)
(☐,☐)	(☐,☐)	(☐,☐)
(☐,☐)		(☐,☐)

/3

Write the amount of water in each jug as millimetres and litres.

40–41.

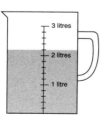

_____ ml

_____ l

42–43.

_____ ml

_____ l

44–45.

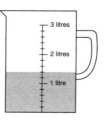

_____ ml

_____ l

46–47.

_____ ml

_____ l

/8

Write how many lines of symmetry there are on each of these shapes.

48. _____

49. _____

50. _____

/3

/50

PAPER 22

Answer these.

| 1. | 39
x 27 | 2. | 73
x 68 | 3. | 36
x 49 | 4. | 72
x 56 |

____   ____   ____   ____

/4

Write a fraction that is equivalent to each of the following decimals.

5. 0.01 _____   **6.** 3.2 _____   **7.** 7.125 _____   **8.** 0.18 _____

9. 0.9 _____   **10.** 0.3 _____   **11.** 0.07 _____   **12.** 2.4 _____

/8

Look at this set of numbers.   **17   14   18   14   19   15   16   17   14**

13. What is the mode for these numbers?

    a) 14   **b)** 17   **c)** 18   **d)** 15

14. What is the median for these numbers?

    a) 14   **b)** 17   **c)** 18   **d)** 16

/2

Write each group of fractions in order starting with the smallest.

15. $\frac{1}{4}$ $\quad$ $\frac{1}{2}$ $\quad$ $\frac{3}{8}$ $\quad$ $\frac{10}{16}$

16. $\frac{1}{6}$ $\quad$ $\frac{3}{4}$ $\quad$ $\frac{1}{3}$ $\quad$ $\frac{6}{12}$

17. $\frac{2}{3}$ $\quad$ $\frac{1}{2}$ $\quad$ $\frac{3}{5}$ $\quad$ $\frac{5}{15}$

18. $\frac{7}{10}$ $\quad$ $\frac{4}{5}$ $\quad$ $\frac{4}{20}$ $\quad$ $\frac{1}{2}$

/4

19–23. Write the decimal number each arrow points to.

19. $\quad$ **20.** $\quad$ **21. 22.** $\quad$ **23.**

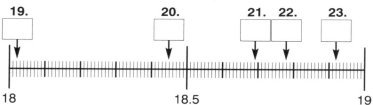

18 $\qquad$ 18.5 $\qquad$ 19

/5

24. What is 75% as a fraction in its lowest terms?

$\quad$ **a)** $\frac{5}{7}$ $\qquad$ **b)** $\frac{1}{4}$ $\qquad$ **c)** $\frac{3}{4}$ $\qquad$ **d)** $\frac{1}{25}$

/1

Circle the container with the greatest amount for each pair.

25. 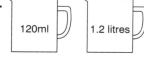 120ml $\quad$ 1.2 litres $\qquad$ **26.** 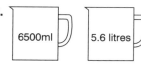 6500ml $\quad$ 5.6 litres

27. 1 litre $\quad$ 100ml $\qquad$ **28.** 4000ml $\quad$ 0.4 litres

/4

Answer these.

29.	**30.**	**31.**	**32.**
78.86	60.52	69.19	78.03
− 39.84	− 43.29	− 28.43	− 58.25

/4

33–37. Look at these triangles and complete the chart by ticking the names.
Remember: some triangles will have more than one name.

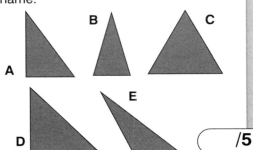

Triangle	A	B	C	D	E
Scalene					
Equilateral					
Isosceles					
Right-angled					

/5

38–43. Calculate the area and perimeter of each shape.

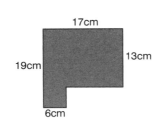

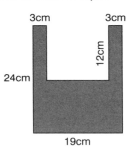

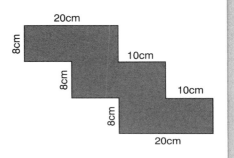

Area = _____ cm²

Perimeter = _____ cm

Area = _____ cm²

Perimeter = _____ cm

Area = _____ cm²

Perimeter = _____ cm

/6

44. How many 3 metre lengths of thread can be cut from a reel of 136 metres?

    a) 46   **b)** 45   **c)** 44   **d)** 43

45. What weight is shown on this scale? _____ kg

46. A train leaves a station at 19.40 and arrives
at its destination 1 hour 25 minutes later.
What is the arrival time for the train? _____

/3

Answer these.

47. 4 | 589   **48.** 8 | 712   **49.** 5 | 886   **50.** 9 | 607

/4

/50

PAPER 23

1. What is the missing number? $216 \div \boxed{} = 30 \, r \, 6$ **a)** 7 **b)** 8 **c)** 6 **d)** 9   /1

2. A square has an area of 144cm². What is the length of each side? _____   /1

3. What type of average shows that 9 is the average for this set of numbers?

    10 5 8 9 10 11 10   **a)** mean **b)** mode **c)** median /1

4. The product of two numbers is 48.
One of the numbers is 16. What is the other number? _____ /1

Circle the greatest weight in each pair.

8.

5.   2750g 2.5kg **6.** 550g 5.5kg **7.** 3kg 2999g

4kg 4g /4

9–16. Write the missing numbers.

  _____ x 10 = 3900   5.23 x _____ = 523   _____ x 100 = 8577   0.81 x _____ = 8.1

  _____ ÷ 100 = 19   8261 ÷ _____ = 82.61   _____ ÷10 = 183   85.7 ÷ _____ = 8.57

/8

17–18. Use **<**, **>** or **=** to make each statement true.

  (5 x 5) + (12 ÷ 4) $\boxed{}$ (8 + 9) + (3 x 3)   27 – (8 x 2) $\boxed{}$ (4 x 5) – (3 x 4)

/2

19. What fraction of this shape is shaded?

  a) $\frac{1}{4}$ **b)** $\frac{3}{4}$

  c) $\frac{2}{3}$ **d)** $\frac{6}{14}$

/1

Answer these.

20. There are 9 buses on a trip, each with 108 passengers.
How many people are there altogether? _____

21. A roll of wire is 23m in length. How much wire will there be in 18 rolls? _____

22. There are 24 pencils in a pack and a school orders 47 packs.
How many pencils will there be altogether? _____

23. A recipe makes 32 cakes each weighing 175g.
What is the total weight of cake mixture in this recipe? _____ /4

Write these percentages as fractions in their lowest terms.

24. 20% → ☐/☐   **25.** 10% → ☐/☐   **26.** 50% → ☐/☐

27. 80% → ☐/☐   **28.** 25% → ☐/☐   **29.** 75% → ☐/☐

/6

30–34. This function machine multiplies. Complete the table of results for the numbers coming out of the function machine.

IN	13	27	44	70	86
OUT					

/5

Write the numbers 2, 3, 4, 5, 6 or 9 in the correct boxes.

35. 75 is divisible by ☐ and ☐

36. 84 is divisible by ☐, ☐, ☐ and ☐

37. 92 is divisible by ☐ and ☐

38. 432 is divisible by ☐, ☐, ☐, ☐ and ☐

/4

39. There are 366 days in a leap year.
How many full weeks are in a year and how many days are left over? _____

/1

Answer these.

40. (19 + 7) – (12 + 5) = ☐   **41.** (9 x 5) + (4 x 6) = ☐

42. (19 – 7) + (28 – 17) = ☐

/3

Read these and write each as a number.

43. three hundred thousand nine hundred and forty-five   _____

44. eighty-nine thousand four hundred and nine   _____

45. two hundred and two thousand and thirty-five   _____

46. five hundred and seventeen thousand two hundred and sixty-one _____

/4

47–50. Which shapes have been opened out flat to make these nets? Match the names.

tetrahedron   square based pyramid   triangular prism   pentagonal based prism

/4

/50

PAPER 24

1. What is the missing number? $216 \div \boxed{} = 70\ r\ 6$ /1

2. How many edges has a pentagonal pyramid got? _____   /1

3. What is the missing number in this sequence?   100   ...   64   49   36

a) 80   **b)** 72   **c)** 81   **d)** 90   /1

4–7. Change these improper fractions to mixed numbers.

$\dfrac{9}{4}$ $\square$ $\dfrac{\square}{\square}$ $\dfrac{17}{3}$ $\square$ $\dfrac{\square}{\square}$ $\dfrac{7}{6}$ $\square$ $\dfrac{\square}{\square}$ $\dfrac{19}{2}$ $\square$ $\dfrac{\square}{\square}$ /4

8–11. Change these mixed numbers to improper fractions.

$3\dfrac{1}{5}$ $\dfrac{\square}{\square}$ $2\dfrac{3}{8}$ $\dfrac{\square}{\square}$ $5\dfrac{1}{2}$ $\dfrac{\square}{\square}$ $6\dfrac{3}{4}$ $\dfrac{\square}{\square}$ /4

12–15. Write < , > or = between each pair of fractions.

$\dfrac{4}{5}$ $\square$ $\dfrac{1}{2}$ $\dfrac{1}{2}$ $\square$ $\dfrac{1}{3}$ $\dfrac{3}{4}$ $\square$ $\dfrac{4}{5}$ $\dfrac{4}{5}$ $\square$ $\dfrac{1}{3}$ /4

Answer these.

16.	6828	**17.**	7128	**18.**	9561
	+ 2742		+ 4675		+ 5918
	——		——		——

/3

What's my number? Work out the mystery number for each of these.

19. When I double my number and then add 9 the answer is 33. _____

20. When I divide my number by 3 and then add 8 the answer is 14. _____

21. When I multiply my number by 8 and then subtract 6 the answer is 18. _____

/4

22. When I divide my number by 5 and then subtract 2 the answer is 6. _____

23–28. Round each price to the nearest pound.

£55.74 _____   £17.08 _____   £18.49 _____

£49.63 _____   £241.93 _____   £309.37 _____

/6

Use a ruler to measure the length of each line accurately in millimetres.

29. ▄▄▄▄▄▄▄▄▄▄▄▄▄▄▄▄▄▄▄▄▄▄▄▄▄   _____mm

30. ▄▄▄▄▄▄▄▄▄▄▄▄   _____mm

31. ▄▄▄▄▄▄▄▄▄   _____mm

/3

32. Which of these numbers is a common multiple of 3 and 8?

  a) 42   **b)** 64   **c)** 72   **d)** 38

/1

33–34. In these sequences each number is double the previous number.
Write the missing numbers.

☐ ☐ 8 16 32 ☐ ☐

☐ ☐ 10 20 40 ☐ ☐

/2

This chart shows the height and weight of a group of men.

35. Write the heights in order, starting with the tallest.

_____ _____ _____ _____

36. Write the weights in order, starting with the heaviest.

_____ _____ _____ _____

Height (m)	1.68	1.79	1.7	1.82
Weight (kg)	80.29	87.37	78.61	87.12

/2

What is the difference in temperature between these pairs of thermometers?

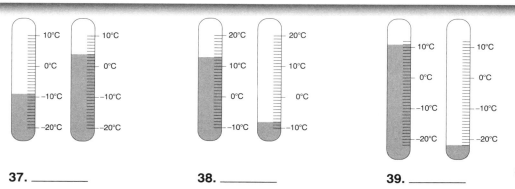

37. _____ **38.** _____ **39.** _____

/3

40. Which angle is approximately 250°? _____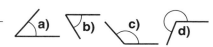

/1

41–42. Circle the correct rule for these.

n	1	2	3	4	5
?	5	10	15	20	25

n	1	2	3	4	5
?	4	7	10	13	16

/2

43–46. Write the factors of these numbers in order, starting with 1.

12 → 1 ☐ ☐ ☐ ☐ ☐

27 → 1 ☐ ☐ ☐

45 → 1 ☐ ☐ ☐ ☐ ☐

36 → 1 ☐ ☐ ☐ ☐ ☐ ☐ ☐ ☐

/4

47. What time is 17.40 using 12-hour time?　　**a)** 7.40pm　**b)** 5.40am
　　　　　　　　　　　　　　　　　　　　　　c) 5.40pm　**d)** 6.40pm

/1

48–49. Draw the lines of symmetry on each shape.

/2

50. What is the area of this rectangle?

_____　6.5cm

9cm

/1

/50

Glossary

acute angle	an angle smaller than a right-angle, so between 0° and 90°
adjacent	near or next to something
anticlockwise	turning in this direction
approximate	a 'rough' answer - near to the real answer
area	the area of a shape is the amount of surface that it covers
axis	(plural is axes) the horizontal and vertical lines on a graph
clockwise	turning in this direction
denominator	bottom number of a fraction, the number of parts it is divided into. Example: $\frac{2}{3}$
difference	the difference between two numbers is the amount that one number is greater than the other. The difference between 18 and 21 is 3
digits	there are 10 digits : 0 1 2 3 4 5 6 7 8 and 9, that make all the numbers we use
divisor	a divisor is a number that another number is divided by. For 32 ÷ 4 = 8, the divisor is 4
edge	where two faces of a solid shape meet Edge
equation	where symbols or letters are used instead of numbers. Example: 3y = 12, so y = 4
equivalent	two numbers or measures are equivalent if they are the same or equal
equivalent fractions	these are equal fractions. Example: $\frac{1}{2} = \frac{2}{4} = \frac{3}{6}$
estimate	is like a good guess
even chance	if an event has an even chance, there is the same chance of it happening as not happening
faces	the flat sides of a solid shape Face
factor	a number that will divide exactly into other numbers. Example: 5 is a factor of 20
formula	a formula (plural is formulae) uses letters or words to give a rule
horizontal	a horizontal line is a straight level line across, in the same direction as the horizon
mean	this is the total divided by the number of items. So the mean of 3, 1, 6 and 2 is (3 + 1 + 6 + 2) ÷ 4 = 3
median	the middle number in an ordered list. Example: 3, 8, 11, 15, 16. The median number is 11
mode	the most common number in a list. Example: 2, 6, 4, 2, 5, 5, 2. The mode is 2

multiple	a multiple is a number made by multiplying together two other numbers
negative number	a number less than zero on the number line
net	the net of a 3D shape is what it looks like when it is opened out flat
numerator	is the top number of a fraction. Example: $\frac{3}{5}$
parallel	lines that are parallel never meet
percentage	this is a fraction out of 100, shown with a % sign
perpendicular	a perpendicular line is one that is at right angles to another line
polygon	any straight sided flat shape
prime number	only have two factors, 1 and itself. For example, 23 is a prime number as it can only be divided exactly by 1 and 23
proportion	this is the same as finding the fraction of the whole amount. Example: the proportion of black cubes is 3 out of 5 or $\frac{3}{5}$ ■ ■ ■ ☐ ☐
protractor	a tool for measuring angles
quotient	this is the number of times that one number will divide into another number. Example: When you divide 18 by 3, the quotient is 6
ratio	This compares one amount with another. Example: the ratio of red cubes to blue cubes is 3:2
remainder	if a number cannot be divided exactly by another number then there is a whole number answer with an amount left over, called a remainder
rounding	rounding a whole number means to change it to the nearest ten, hundred or thousand to give an approximate number. Decimal numbers can be rounded to the nearest whole number, tenth or hundredth
sequence	a list of numbers which usually have a pattern. They are often numbers written in order
square number	numbers multiplied by themselves make square numbers. Example 4 x 4 = 16. The first five square numbers are 1, 4, 9, 16 and 25
symmetrical	when two halves of a shape or pattern are identical
vertical	a line that is straight up or down, at right angles to a horizontal line
vertices	(single – vertex) These are the corners of 3D shapes, where edges meet

Vertex ──→

Progress grid

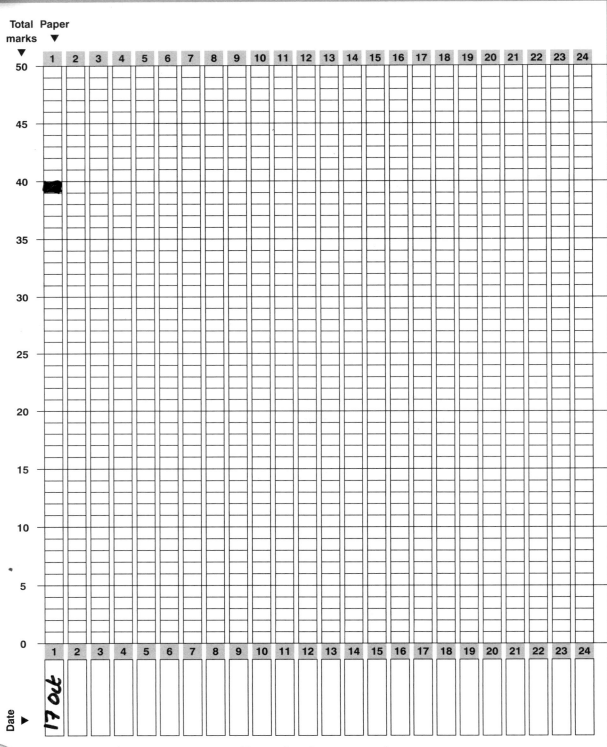

Now colour in your score!